Filters with Helical and Folded Helical Resonators

The Artech House Microwave Library

Filters with Helical and Folded Helical Resonators

Peter Vizmuller

Library of Congress Cataloging-in-Publication Data

Vizmuller, Peter, 1954-
    Filters with helical and folded helical resonators.

    Bibliography: p.
    Includes index.
    1. Microwave filters. 2. Radio resonators.
I. Title.
TK7872.F5V59 1987   621.3815'324   87-1043
ISBN 0-89006-244-7

International Standard Book Number: 0-89006-244-7
Library of Congress Catalog Card Number: 87-1043

10 9 8 7 6 5 4 3 2 1

Contents

Preface

The use of helical resonators in radio frequency applications represents a well known technology, yet a few fundamental problems remain. The purpose of this book is to address these problems and also to examine two new classes of resonators; one produces a slightly higher unloaded quality factor (Q) and the other one offers a partial solution to the reresonance problem associated with conventional helical resonators.

Following a brief chapter on background information with a filter design example, Chapter 2 examines several different models of the helix electromagnetic field. Field expressions for the most useful model are derived in Appendix II from Maxwell's equations in cylindrical coordinates and a set of simplified boundary conditions. These field expressions form the theoretical basis for understanding the behavior of helical resonators and are used to find dominant electric and magnetic field components, and to examine different coupling mechanisms and their effect on filter characteristics.

Several methods for extending the bandwidth are presented in Chapter 3 and a constraint of constant unloaded Q is found to be necessary for filters having a bandwidth that remains constant with tuning. Variation of filter bandwidth with tuning and varactor-tuned filters are examined in Chapter 4.

The problem of temperature and mechanical stability of helical resonator filters is covered in Chapter 6 and is illustrated by several examples of practical resonator construction, using a variety of common materials. Two solutions to this problem are found, one involving a careful selection of materials to match various expansion coefficients, the other one dependent on mechanical rigidity of the resonator top with respect to the tuning mechanism.

Also, two new types of helical resonators are introduced in Chapters 5 and 7. The first, a tapered resonator is found to have improved unloaded Q, while the other one, called a folded resonator, has the advantage of variable reresonant frequencies, which can be chosen independently of the fundamental resonance, thus presenting a design tool with which the reresonance of a filter can be placed at any desired frequency between three and four times the fundamental.

A set of computer programs to aid in designing helical filters is presented at the end of the book in Appendix III, together with some worked-out examples. The inclusion of computer programs signifies that computer programs are valuable tools in the hands of a filter designer.

I have tried not to dwell too much on well known aspects of helical filter design, tuning, or construction, because the interested reader can easily look up the relevant details as referenced in the bibliography. A thorough search through periodicals and patents relevant to this topic was undertaken for three reasons: to give proper credit to investigators working in a given area; to enable others to research an interesting topic in more detail; and to avoid duplication of effort which can result when solutions to common problems are sought by several investigators.

I would like to take this opportunity to express my gratitude to Professor V. M. Ristic of the University of Toronto and Mr. G. N. Popovski, formerly of Motorola Canada, for their support during the course of this work, as well as to Mr. B. Compson and Mr. W. Solo of Motorola Canada for their permission to publish this work and for the use of Motorola's computer resources. My wife Suzanne and our children, Andrew and Catherine, deserve special thanks for their patience and understanding.

Chapter 1
Introduction

Helical resonator filters find most of their usefulness in the frequency range where conventional lumped-element filter components lose their desirable characteristics (unloaded Q, convenient capacitance or inductance value, physical size, *et cetera*) to realize a given filter specification. In practice, this means that helical resonators become the preferred elements in bandpass and band-rejection filters of a center frequency from several tens of MHz to about 2 GHz, and of a bandwidth from about 0.5% to more than 50%. In the lower frequency range, helical resonators compete with discrete LC, crystal, and SAW filters, while toward higher frequencies, competing filter components are air or dielectric-loaded coaxial, microstrip, and stripline resonators.

In its most conventional form, a typical bandpass filter consists of several helical resonators coupled to each other through openings, called apertures, in the walls separating them, as shown schematically in Fig. 1 (coil forms and other mechanical details have been omitted for clarity). The helical resonators are quarter-wave sections of a shielded helical transmission line, grounded (short-circuited to shield) at one end and open-circuited at the other end. The helix is almost always of circular cross section, while the shield enclosing it can be of either circular or square cross section.

Input and output coupling to the filter is provided by taps to the appropriate impedance points on the helix. Tuning is most easily accomplished by capacitive loading at the open-circuited end, which

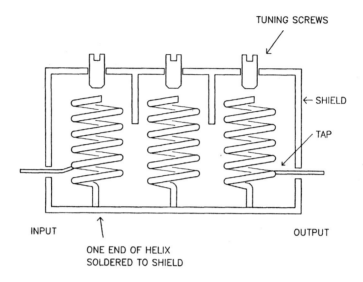

TUNING SCREWS

← SHIELD

TAP

INPUT

OUTPUT

ONE END OF HELIX
SOLDERED TO SHIELD

Fig. 1 Typical Bandpass Filter Arrangement

is often conveniently done by an adjustable tuning screw. The aperture size and location influence the bandwidth, while the input-output taps predominantly provide impedance matching to source and load.

Helical filters are mostly designed for Butterworth response, since the lowest unloaded Q is required to realize a given midband loss for this class of filters. Other forms of coupling and tuning are, of course, possible and will be discussed later.

The first design guidelines for helical resonators (without direct reference to filters) were published in 1959 [1]. Only resonators with shield of circular cross section were considered, where optimum shield diameter with respect to unloaded Q was determined experimentally. The use of helical resonators for VHF bandpass filters was described in a paper by Zverev and Blinchikoff [2], which together with Zverev's *Handbook of Filter Synthesis* [3] supplies the background information required for most helical resonator filter designs, including a comprehensive treatment of unloaded Q requirements. The use of helical resonators was also extended to linear phase filters, bandstop filters, multiplexers, and frequency multipliers, as well as commercial two-way communication and amateur radio [5–7, 22].

Summarizing the developments in helical filter design, below is a brief outline of a typical bandpass filter design procedure, using the design of a 490 MHz filter as an example. The objective is to design a Butterworth filter of 490 MHz center frequency, 14 MHz 1 dB bandwidth, 1.0 dB insertion loss with a skirt selectivity greater than 40 dB at 450 MHz.

1. From the given filter specifications, determine the number of sections and minimum unloaded Q to realize a Butterworth filter (see Appendix III). For our example, using the results obtained by running the BUTTERWORTH program in Appendix III, a three-resonator filter of 17.2 MHz 3 dB bandwidth, constructed of resonators with unloaded Q of 500, should meet the given filter specifications.

2. Translate the unloaded Q and frequency of operation to a set of dimensions for an optimum helical resonator (see Appendices I and III). Assuming we will be using resonators with a shield of square cross section, the Helical-s program calculates that a volume of 1.15 cm $\times$ 1.15 cm $\times$ 1.83 cm for each of the three resonators will result in an unloaded Q of 600. All the other mechanical dimensions such as the wire gauge, helix pitch, number of turns, *et cetera* are supplied by this program as well.

3. From the ratio of Q unloaded/Q minimum, number of sections and filter bandwidth, look up a set of normalized coupling coefficients (Zverev, pp. 341, 518). For our filter, the ratio of unloaded Q to loaded Q is about 20 and, therefore, using predistortion $q_1 = 0.8041$, $k_{12} = 0.7687$, $k_{23} = 0.6582$, $q_3 = 1.4156$.

4. Adjust input tap and aperture dimensions to satisfy coupling coefficients. A general, systematic procedure does not exist for obtaining the aperture dimensions for a given coupling

coefficient; the aperture dimensions have to be obtained em-
pirically by measurements on the actual filter. Therefore, the
filter must be assembled at this point to determine the aperture
dimensions using the following method: For a 50 ohm system
and Q unloaded $\gg Q$ minimum (usually true in practice), the
coupling coefficients can most conveniently be measured by
the set-up shown in Fig. 2. First, all resonators are detuned
and the first resonator is tuned for peak reading on channel B
of the vector voltmeter at the desired frequency. Then the tap
is adjusted for the correct loaded Q as a fraction of desired
filter 3 dB bandwidth (given by previously mentioned tables).
Loaded Q is measured in the usual way by varying the signal
generator frequency until the reading on channel B drops by
3 dB on either side of resonance. The frequency difference
between the 3 dB down points, when divided into the resonant
frequency, gives the loaded Q. For the filter of our example,
adjust the input tap until the frequency difference between the
3 dB down points is $q_1 \times$ BW3 dB $= 0.8041 \times 17.2 =$
13.83 MHz, then reverse filter and adjust the output tap for a
frequency difference of $1.4156 \times 17.2 = 24.35$ MHz. The
next step is to return to resonance of the first coil and tune
the second resonator for a minimum on channel B. Then vary
signal generator frequency and locate two peak readings on
channel B. The difference in frequency between the two is
related to the coupling coefficient; the aperture size should be
adjusted until the correct frequency difference as a function
of desired filter bandwidth (again given in tables) is obtained.
In our example, when the second resonator is tuned for minimum reading at 490 MHz, two peaks will be observed in the
frequency response on channel B. The aperture dimensions
between the first and second resonators should be adjusted
until the frequency difference of the peaks is $k_{12} \times$ BW3 dB
$= 0.7687 \times 17.2 = 13.22$ MHz. Similarly, when the filter
is turned around to use the output as the input, the other
aperture dimensions should be adjusted to obtain a frequency
difference of $k_{23} \times$ BW3 dB $= 0.6582 \times 17.2 = 11.32$
MHz between the two peaks. The unused resonator should

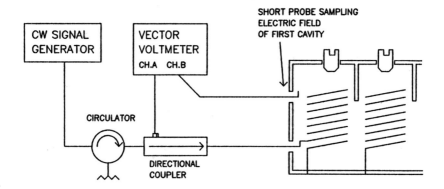

Fig. 2 Measurement of Coupling Coefficients

always be detuned from resonance as far as possible. For multisection filters, when tuning the nth resonator, n frequency peaks will be observed on channel B. At this point it should be noted that the spacing of the n frequency peaks is not only related to the coupling coefficient, but also to the unloaded Q, if not high enough. In this case, predistortion or some other technique should be used to relate the frequency difference of the peaks to the coupling coefficient [27].

Tuning the final filter can be done by one of the following methods:

1. For small percentage bandwidths, "power tuning" can be used, where all resonators are tuned (repeatedly) for maximum transmission of power.

2. For small or moderate percentage bandwidths, Dishal's method or "peak-dip" tuning can be used [3, 4].

3. Frequency swept transmission measurement—tune for lowest insertion loss in passband.

4. Frequency swept reflection measurement—tune for highest return loss across passband.

If the source or load impedances are not 50 ohms, the tap location can be recalculated, but in practice it is found that empirical adjustment of tap location for best return loss yields faster and more satisfactory results. Another method of measuring intercavity coupling is to monitor the phase of the input reflection coefficient when the output port is terminated in a short circuit [16]. This method is potentially the more accurate, and also has application in tuning a complex filter.

If optimum response is sought from a helical filter, the physical construction techniques become rather important. Any of the following symptoms indicate problems with construction, the presence of unwanted coupling, or suppression of desired coupling between resonators, as given in Table 1.

Table 1

Symptom	*Probable Cause*
High insertion loss	Contamination of surface to reduce Q. Faulty ground at end of helix or faulty tap connection.
Passband ripple	Incorrect impedance loading of filter input or output. Helix axis not parallel to walls.
Low return loss	Incorrect loading of filter. Incorrect tap location.
Insufficient stopband attenuation	Filter covers do not make good electrical contact. Stray coupling is present through ground loops.

Figures 3 and 4 illustrate the three-resonator filter designed using the procedure presented on the previous pages. The total volume is approximately 1.5 cm × 2.2 cm × 4.5 cm; when constructed of copper the unloaded Q is approximately 580, measured insertion loss is 1.0 dB, and 3 dB bandwidth is 17.2 MHz centered at 490 MHz.

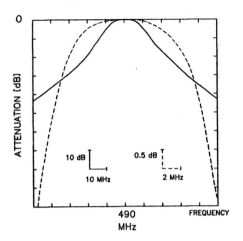

Fig. 3 Three-Resonator UHF Filter

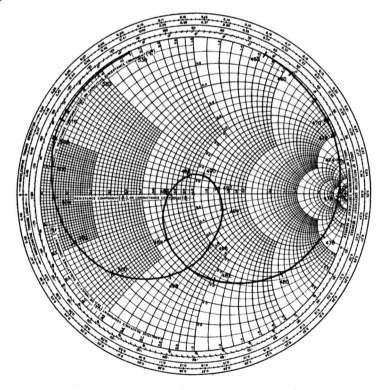

Fig. 4 Input Impedance of Filter of Fig. 3

Chapter 2
Field Configuration and Coupling Mechanism

The initial research into the electromagnetic fields associated with a coaxial line with helical inner conductor was intimately connected with traveling wave tube (TWT) development [8–10, 14]. Even though the requirements for an optimum TWT helix are different from those of an optimum quarter-wave helical resonator, the basic assumptions in evaluating the electromagnetic field of a helical transmission line are applicable to both. The fundamental problem involves finding explicit expressions, or methods for evaluating the 12 components governing the behavior of electromagnetic field on a helical structure.

Historically, four basic physical models were used to approximate the helix in applying Maxwell's equations and the appropriate boundary conditions. Presented below is an overview of these four methods. Before plunging into Bessel function mathematics, however, let us pause briefly and ask why knowledge of the fields contained in a resonator is important, what insight can be gained into the operation of a bandpass filter, and whether practical results can be obtained from the lengthy mathematical expressions.

First of all, a knowledge of the propagation constant yields the electrical length and relates the size of a $\lambda/4$ helical line to its resonant frequency. The propagation constant is also needed for estimating the unloaded Q. Next, the relative magnitudes of the fields indicate which component is the dominant coupling mechanism for what size, location, and orientation of the aperture, or other coupling method. Can the fields be modified by using dielectrics, ferrites, or metal structures to improve performance? How sensitive are the fields to mechanical deformation (such as temperature variation)? Does the field intensity vary along a resonator chain? Also, we can determine where the highest surface current is flowing and thus determine where a seam or surface discontinuity should not be placed in constructing a filter—some surfaces might have to be silver-plated for greatest improvement of unloaded Q.

From the above, it is clear that knowledge of the fields has its place in understanding and using helical structures. Let us, therefore, return to the four models of the helix.

2.1 SHEATH HELIX [8, 11–13]

This is a model in which the helix is represented by a cylinder that conducts only in a direction specified by the pitch angle of the helix ψ. No current can flow perpendicular to this direction (see Fig. 5). A solution to Maxwell's equations in cylindrical coordinates with the following boundary conditions [8, 15] yields equations (2.1) to (2.12).

Boundary conditions:

1. Tangential electric field must be perpendicular to helix direction at $r = a$.

2. Tangential electric field must be continuous across cylinder.

3. Tangential magnetic field must be continuous across cylinder.

4. At $r = b$, tangential electric field = 0.

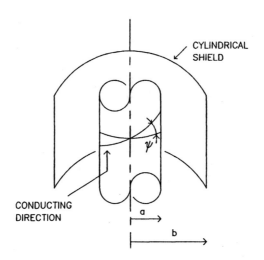

Fig. 5 Sheath Helix Enclosed in a Cylindrical Shield

2.1.1 Without External Shield, in Free Space

Inside Helix

$$E_z = AI_0(\gamma r)e^{j(\omega t - \beta z)} \tag{2.1}$$

$$E_r = jA \frac{\beta}{\gamma} I_1(\gamma r)e^{j(\omega t - \beta z)} \tag{2.2}$$

$$E_\theta = -A \frac{I_0(\gamma a)}{I_1(\gamma a)}(\tan \psi)I_1(\gamma r)e^{j(\omega t - \beta z)} \tag{2.3}$$

$$H_z = -jA \frac{\gamma}{\omega\mu} \frac{I_0(\gamma a)}{I_1(\gamma a)}(\tan \psi)I_0(\gamma r)e^{j(\omega t - \beta z)} \tag{2.4}$$

$$H_r = A \frac{\beta}{\omega\mu} \frac{I_0(\gamma a)}{I_1(\gamma a)}(\tan \psi)I_1(\gamma r)e^{j(\omega t - \beta z)} \tag{2.5}$$

$$H_\theta = jA \frac{\omega\epsilon}{\gamma} I_1(\gamma r)e^{j(\omega t - \beta z)} \tag{2.6}$$

12

Outside Helix

$$E_z = A \frac{I_0(\gamma a)}{K_0(\gamma a)} K_0(\gamma r) e^{j(\omega t - \beta z)} \tag{2.7}$$

$$E_r = -jA \frac{\beta}{\gamma} \frac{I_0(\gamma a)}{K_0(\gamma a)} K_1(\gamma r) e^{j(\omega t - \beta z)} \tag{2.8}$$

$$E_\theta = -A \frac{I_0(\gamma a)}{K_1(\gamma a)} (\tan \psi) K_1(\gamma r) e^{j(\omega t - \beta z)} \tag{2.9}$$

$$H_z = jA \frac{\gamma}{\omega\mu} \frac{I_0(\gamma a)}{K_1(\gamma a)} (\tan \psi) K_0(\gamma r) e^{j(\omega t - \beta z)} \tag{2.10}$$

$$H_r = A \frac{\beta}{\omega\mu} \frac{I_0(\gamma a)}{K_1(\gamma a)} (\tan \psi) K_1(\gamma r) e^{j(\omega t - \beta z)} \tag{2.11}$$

$$H_\theta = -jA \frac{\omega\epsilon}{\gamma} \frac{I_0(\gamma a)}{K_0(\gamma a)} K_1(\gamma r) e^{j(\omega t - \beta z)} \tag{2.12}$$

Propagation Constant

The propagation constant is determined from the following relation (dispersion relation):

$$(\gamma a)^2 \frac{I_0(\gamma a) K_0(\gamma a)}{I_1(\gamma a) K_1(\gamma a)} = (\beta_0 a \cot \psi)^2 \tag{2.13}$$

where

A = arbitrary amplitude constant

I_0 = modified Bessel function of the first kind, order zero

I_1 = modified Bessel function of the first kind, order one

K_0 = modified Bessel function of the second kind, order zero

K_1 = modified Bessel function of the second kind, order one

γ^2 = $\beta^2 - \beta_0^2$ radial propagation constant

β_0 = $\dfrac{\omega}{c}$ free space propagation constant

β = $\dfrac{\omega}{v_p}$ guided propagation constant

ω = angular frequency $(2\pi f)$

c = speed of light in free space

v_p = phase velocity of guided wave

r, θ, z = cylindrical coordinate components

a = radius of sheath helix

ψ = pitch angle of helix $\rightarrow$ conducting direction

μ = permeability of free space

ϵ = permittivity of free space

2.1.2 With External, Cylindrical, Perfectly Conducting Shield in Free Space

Field expressions for this case are derived in Appendix II.

Inside Helix

These expressions are the same as equations (2.1) to (2.6).

Outside Helix

$$E_z = A\,\Delta_0 \left[K_0(\gamma r) - \frac{K_0(\gamma b)}{I_0(\gamma b)} I_0(\gamma r) \right] e^{j(\omega t - \beta z)} \qquad (2.14)$$

$$E_r = -jA\,\frac{\beta}{\gamma}\,\Delta_0 \left[K_1(\gamma r) + \frac{K_0(\gamma b)}{I_0(\gamma b)} I_1(\gamma r) \right] e^{j(\omega t - \beta z)} \qquad (2.15)$$

$$E_\theta = -A\,(\tan \psi)\,\Delta_1 \left[K_1(\gamma r) - \frac{K_1(\gamma b)}{I_1(\gamma b)} I_1(\gamma r) \right] e^{j(\omega t - \beta z)} \qquad (2.16)$$

$$H_z = jA\,\frac{\gamma}{\omega\mu}\,(\tan\psi)\,\Delta_1\left[K_0(\gamma r) + \frac{K_1(\gamma b)}{I_1(\gamma b)}I_0(\gamma r)\right]e^{j(\omega t - \beta z)} \qquad (2.17)$$

$$H_r = A\,\frac{\beta}{\omega\mu}\,(\tan\psi)\,\Delta_1\left[K_1(\gamma r) - \frac{K_1(\gamma b)}{I_1(\gamma b)}I_1(\gamma r)\right]e^{j(\omega t - \beta z)} \qquad (2.18)$$

$$H_\theta = -jA\,\frac{\omega\epsilon}{\gamma}\,\Delta_0\left[K_1(\gamma r) + \frac{K_0(\gamma b)}{I_0(\gamma b)}I_1(\gamma r)\right]e^{j(\omega t - \beta z)} \qquad (2.19)$$

Propagation Constant

$$(\beta_0 a\cot\psi)^2 = (\gamma a)^2\frac{I_0(\gamma a)}{I_1(\gamma a)}\frac{\Delta_1}{\Delta_0} \qquad (2.20)$$

b = radius of cylindrical shield

$$\Delta_0 = \frac{I_0(\gamma a)I_0(\gamma b)}{I_0(\gamma b)K_0(\gamma a) - I_0(\gamma a)K_0(\gamma b)} \qquad (2.21)$$

$$\Delta_1 = \frac{I_0(\gamma a)I_1(\gamma b)}{I_1(\gamma b)K_1(\gamma a) - I_1(\gamma a)K_1(\gamma b)} \qquad (2.22)$$

for $b>a$, positive constants determined by geometry

$$\lim_{b\to\infty}\Delta_0 = \frac{I_0(\gamma a)}{K_0(\gamma a)}, \qquad \lim_{b\to\infty}\Delta_1 = \frac{I_0(\gamma a)}{K_1(\gamma a)}$$

2.1.3 Special Cases

Special cases of the above two boundary conditions can be found in the literature as follows:

Lossy helical surface surrounded by lossless shield [15];
Different media inside and outside [11, 13];
Helical conductor between coaxial conductive cylinders [12].

2.2 ASSUMED CURRENT DISTRIBUTION OF AN INFINITELY THIN HELIX [10]

In this model it is assumed that the helix is excited by a monochromatic electromagnetic field which induces a sinusoidal current along the helix. With the aid of the retarded vector potential derived from this assumed current distribution, the electric and magnetic fields outside the helix are derived as infinite sums involving modified Bessel functions of the second kind (K_n). The expression for longitudinal electric field will be given below for illustration:

$$E_z = 4\pi(\beta_0^2 - \beta^2)\alpha F e^{j\beta z} \sum_{n=-\infty}^{\infty} I_n(\Gamma_n a)K_n(\Gamma_n r)$$

$$\exp[jn(\psi - z/\alpha)] - 4\pi j\beta F e^{j\beta z} \sum_{n=-\infty}^{\infty} jn I_n(\Gamma_n a)K_n(\Gamma_n r)\exp[jn(\psi - z/\alpha)] \qquad (2.23)$$

$$\Gamma_n = \left[\left(\beta - \frac{n}{\alpha}\right)^2 - \beta_0^2\right]^{1/2}$$

$$F = \frac{-Ie^{-j\omega t}}{4\pi j\omega\epsilon\alpha}$$

$$I = \sum_{-\infty}^{\infty} 4\pi e^{jn\psi} I_n(\Gamma_n a)K_n(\Gamma_n r)$$

α = parameter defining helix

  in cylindrical coordinates

$r = a,$ $z = \alpha\psi$

An interesting observation can be drawn from this model. Although retarded potentials were invoked for the field derivation, this model predicts no net radial flow of energy (no radiation perpendicular to helix axis).

2.3 EXACT FORMULATION OF BOUNDARY CONDITIONS USING HELICAL COORDINATES [17]

In this coordinate system both Maxwell's equations and boundary conditions can be formulated exactly; however, since the coordinate system is nonorthogonal, the equations cannot be solved by the separation of variables and only approximate solutions can be obtained. Nevertheless, the fields close to the wire itself can be examined successfully using this technique. Figure 6 shows the helical coordinates.

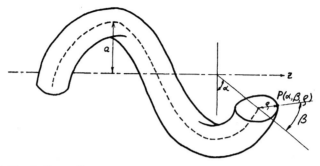

Fig. 6 Helical Coordinates

Parameters from Fig. 6 are

α = arc length along center line of helix measured in such units that α increases by 2π in traversing a single turn;

β = angle measured from a line perpendicular to both the z-axis and center line of helix;

ρ = distance from center line of helix.

The expressions for Maxwell's equations in helical coordinates, as well as the relationship between helical unit vectors and cylindrical coordinate unit vectors, can be found in [17]. The boundary conditions for an unshielded helix take a particularly simple form: $E_\alpha = E_\beta = H_\rho = 0$ at ρ = radius of wire.

2.3.1   Tape Helix [14, 18]

Here, the helix is modeled as a thin tape of width δ wound on a cylindrical form as shown in Fig. 7.

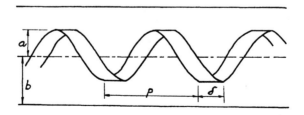

Fig. 7 Tape Helix Enclosed in Cylindrical Shield

The structure now has periodic translational as well as rotational symmetry, so that the fields show periodic z-dependence of the form:

$$e^{-j\beta z} e^{-jm(2\pi/p)z}$$

The next step in the analysis is to assume a certain current distribution on the tape, which can have only two components: longitudinal and transverse, because the tape is assumed to be infinitely thin (zero radial dimension). The two components of current density are then expanded into Fourier series, each term giving rise to a component of electric and magnetic field. Thus, each field component is an infinite superposition of partial fields arising from Fourier expansion of tape currents.

If one assumes a traveling wave (sinusoidal) form of tape current, then the field components are of the following form (only the longitudinal $\bar{E}$ component outside the helix will be given here for illustration):

$$E_z = \sum_{m=-\infty}^{\infty} j \sqrt{\frac{\mu}{\epsilon} \frac{(P_m a)^2}{\beta_0 a}} I_m(P_m a) \left[\frac{K_m(P_m b)}{I_m(P_m b)} I_m(P_m r) - K_m(P_m r) \right]$$

$$\times \left[\frac{m h_m a}{(P_m a)^2} K\psi_m - Kz_m \right]$$

$$\exp(jm\psi) \exp(-jh\,m\,z) \tag{2.24}$$

P_m = radial propagation constants

$h_m = \beta + 2\pi m/p$ axial propagation constants

$K\psi_m, Kz_m$ = Fourier coefficients of transverse and longitudinal components of current density on tape

where a, b, p are illustrated in Fig. 7.

The equations giving the propagation constants P_m take different form depending on the geometry (i.e., different simplifying assumptions are used) and can be found in [18]. The condition for optimum Q of a resonator in this model requires that $p = 2\delta$.

2.4 SUMMARY

From the preceding four models, it is clear that none of them can be readily applied to a general engineering problem because the more exact models are burdened with complicated mathematics and the simple models lack the precision one would like in a detailed analysis. Therefore, the usefulness of each model has to be limited according to the simplifying assumptions made, and the limitations should always be kept in mind when applying a certain model. For example, we can be quite confident when evaluating coupling fields distant from the helix using the sheath model, yet we cannot make deductions about the dependence of unloaded Q on the wire size. To make deductions about the dependence, helix losses can be approached by using helical coordinates or the tape helix model. As a consequence, the remainder of this chapter will be devoted to interpreting the coupling fields using the sheath model equations, bearing in mind that predictions made about fields close to the helix, or near a helix of coarse pitch, might or might not be true.

Let us now examine the relative amplitudes and phases of the field components described in equations (2.1) to (2.20) and determine the conditions under which these equations can be applied to a helical resonator. From a closer look at these equations, the following observations can be made:

1. Field configuration is definitely not transverse electromagnetic mode (TEM).
2. Fields inside the sheath helix are unchanged by the presence of an external shield.
3. E_r, H_z, and H_θ change phase from the interior to the exterior of a helix.
4. Because all the field components have the form of a traveling wave, a quarter-wave resonator can be considered as a section of transmission line open-circuited at one end and short-circuited at the other. Therefore, the field components will show variation as $\sin \beta z$ and $\cos \beta z$, $0 < z < \pi/2\beta$, with electric field maximum at the open end and magnetic field maximum at the short-circuited end. Of course, this is only true in the ideal

case; if there is substantial capacitive loading at the open-circuited end, some current will flow in the top few turns and thus magnetic field will not be zero there.

5. Equations (2.1) to (2.20) contain a multiplying factor A, which was assumed constant. In a real resonator, A will depend on frequency because Q also is a function of frequency given approximately as [13]

$$Q \doteq 44bf^{1/2} \qquad (2.25)$$

where

Q = unloaded Q of optimal cylindrical
   resonator (i.e., $b/a \approx 2$)

b = shield radius (cm)

f = resonant frequency (MHz)

To obtain further information from the equations, let us consider an approximate numerical comparison. Let us assume that the coupling fields across an aperture are similar to fields surrounding an unshielded helix at the same radial distance. Consider two quarter-wave resonators whose dimensions correspond to optimum Q and are the same, except for the helix pitch, such that one resonates at $f_1 = 160$ MHz and the other at $f_2 = 400$ MHz. Because the lengths of helical transmission line are the same in both cases, $\beta_1 = \beta_2$.

Using Table 2 (pitch angles ψ determined by experiment), let us proceed to calculate the field components at a distance $b = 6.0$ mm, omitting the scalar factor A and $\sin \beta z$ variation for simplicity. Substituting the given values into equations (2.7) to (2.22), the values given in Table 3 are obtained (electrical field in units of V/m, magnetic field A/m). To obtain meaningful comparison between electric and magnetic fields and to determine which fields dominate, the quantities shown in parentheses were calculated as $\epsilon_0 E_n^2$ and $\mu_0 H_n^2$, which are proportional to the energy density contained in a particular field component and are shown in units of 10^{-12} J/m^3.

Table 2

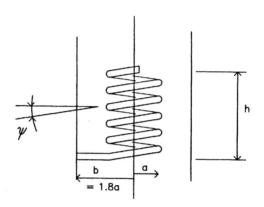

= 1.8a

Case 1—VHF	Case 2—UHF

$$a_1 = 3.3 \, \text{mm}$$
$$a_2 = a_1 = 3.3 \, \text{mm}$$

$$b_1 = 6.0 \, \text{mm}$$
$$b_2 = b_1 = 6.0 \, \text{mm}$$

$$f_1 = 160 \, \text{MHz}$$
$$f_2 = 400 \, \text{MHz}$$

$$\omega_1 = 10^9 \, \text{s}^{-1}$$
$$\omega_2 = 2.5 \times 10^9 \, \text{s}^{-1}$$

$$h_1 = \frac{\lambda_1}{4} = 20 \, \text{mm}$$
$$h_1 = h_2 = \frac{\lambda_2}{4} = 20 \, \text{mm}$$

$$\beta_1 = \frac{2\pi}{\lambda_1} = 78.5 \, \text{m}^{-1}$$
$$\beta_2 = \frac{2\pi}{\lambda_2} = 78.5 \, \text{m}^{-1}$$

$$\beta_{01} = \frac{\omega_1}{c} = 3.33 \, \text{m}^{-1}$$
$$\beta_{02} = \frac{\omega_2}{c} = 8.33 \, \text{m}^{-1}$$

$$\psi_1 = 2°$$
$$\psi_2 = 7°$$

It now becomes quite apparent that the radial electric field dominates in both the shielded and unshielded cases. Furthermore, the presence of a shield markedly increases the energy density. The difference between this increase of stored energy and losses introduced in the shield is a maximum for the optimum ratio of b/a [13]. Because the radial electric field dominates in both the shielded

Table 3

(a) Without shield at $r = b = 6$ mm

	VHF		UHF	
E_z	0.66	(3.86)	0.66	(3.86)
E_r	$-j1.21$	(13.0)	$-j1.22$	(13.2)
E_θ	-0.018	(0.003)	-0.062	(0.03)
H_z	$j6.0 \times 10^{-4}$	(0.45)	$j8.4 \times 10^{-4}$	(0.9)
H_r	11.0×10^{-4}	(1.52)	15.5×10^{-4}	(3.0)
H_θ	$-j1.4 \times 10^{-4}$	(0.02)	$-j3.4 \times 10^{-4}$	(0.14)

(b) With shield at $b = 6$ mm, fields at $r = b$

	VHF		UHF	
E_z	0		0	
E_r	$-j3.96$	(139)	$-j3.98$	(140)
E_θ	0		0	
H_z	$j75 \times 10^{-4}$	(70.9)	$j93 \times 10^{-4}$	(109)
H_r	0		0	
H_θ	$-j4.1 \times 10^{-4}$	(0.2)	$-j10 \times 10^{-4}$	(1.3)

---

and unshielded cases, we can safely assume that when the aperture for coupling between resonators is placed near the ungrounded end, the coupling mechanism can be modeled as a small capacitance as shown in Fig. 8. In fact, it can be argued that when apertures are used for coupling, it is difficult to get coupling that is not capacitive. Figure 9 illustrates why this is so. The relative energy density contained in the dominant electric and magnetic field components is plotted as a function of distance along a $\lambda/4$ resonator, taking into account the $\sin \beta z$ variation of fields and thus $\sin^2 \beta z$ variation of energy density at resonance. In addition, Fig. 9 shows that at $f_0 = 160$ MHz the radial electric field dominates for approximately 80% of the resonator length. It is only in the lower 21% of the resonator that H_r can be considered dominant. What this means in practice is that if a helical resonator has 26 turns, H_r is dominant

22

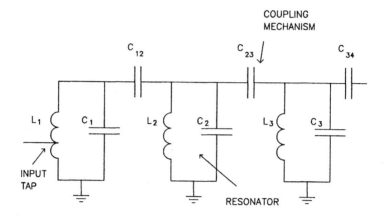

Fig. 8 Equivalent Circuit of a Bandpass Filter

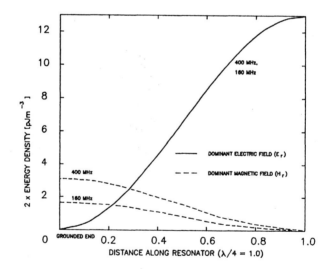

Fig. 9 Relative Energy Density Along a Resonator

in the bottom 5.5 turns only. An aperture of such small dimensions would probably not provide enough coupling for a moderate bandwidth filter. Two additional factors complicating the magnetic field distribution are tap placement and grounding arrangement, which affect the geometry in the location of H_r maximum. At 400 MHz the region of H_r dominance is increased to 28.5% primarily because the pitch angle increases.

It should be pointed out here that the ability to choose between inductive and capacitive coupling using apertures is greatly dependent on the unloaded Q. For miniature resonators, where the unloaded Q is less than 300, the predominant coupling must be capacitive; because most of the stored energy is contained in the radial electric field, the magnetic fields are not strong enough to transfer sufficient energy for a realistic filter, as mentioned. For high Q resonators, this is not the case, and predominantly inductive coupling can be obtained by specially shaped apertures, because the fields are much stronger due to the higher Q. Also, for resonators tuned by discrete capacitors or large tuning screws, most of the electric field will be confined to the capacitor, and magnetic fields become more important.

Now we are in a position to explain why most helical filters in practice are observed to have assymetrical skirts or transition bands in the sense that the slope of the frequency response is greater on the low-frequency side than the high-frequency side. This effect is also known as *skewing* of the filter response.

Theoretically, the skirts of a Butterworth bandpass filter are symmetrical when the frequency axis is shown on a logarithmic scale. If such an ideal filter is examined with a sweeper and a spectrum analyzer having a linear frequency axis, the slope on the low-frequency side would appear greater because, in going from a logarithmic scale to a linear scale, the low frequencies appear compressed and the higher frequencies appear expanded. Helical filters show skewing that is even more pronounced, as illustrated by Fig. 10. The reason for this can be explained by two factors having

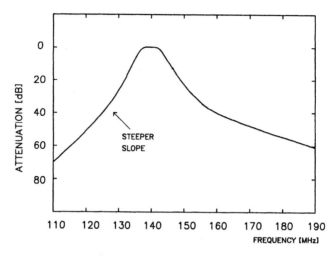

Fig. 10 Skewing of Filter Response

relative importance depending on filter bandwidth, size, and frequency of operation. The first factor is the capacitive coupling previously mentioned, whereby the coupling increases as frequency is increased. The second factor is that the unloaded Q also increases with frequency. This means that when considering two frequencies off resonance, f_L being lower and f_H being higher, such that $\sqrt{f_L \times f_H} = f_0$ (center frequency of filter), the energy stored at f_H is higher than at f_L due to the higher Q. Not only is the stored energy greater at f_H, but a larger portion of it is transferred to the next resonator because of the capacitive nature of the coupling mechanism. Using the filter of Fig. 10 as an example, the attenuation at 30 MHz below center frequency, according to tables of Butterworth filters or Appendix III, should be in the neighborhood of 55 dB, whereas the measured value was 70 dB, which represents a significant difference that could be exploited in practice to decrease the number of resonators required in a filter. Inductive coupling would skew the filter response the other way. Figure 11 illustrates a filter identical to that of Fig. 10, except that due to a fault in construction, the base on which the coils were mounted did not make a good electrical contact to the cover, which contained

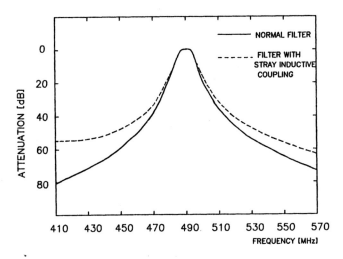

Fig. 11 Filter with Stray Inductive Coupling

the resonator walls, apertures, and tuning screws. The result was that, in the passband, capacitive coupling was still dominant and the bandwidth did not change; in the stopband, however, stray ground currents provided additional inductive coupling which became dominant and, in addition to providing greater attenuation on the high-frequency side, destroyed the ultimate attenuation capability of the filter.

The preceding discussion implies that to get a filter with symmetrical skirts, it is not only necessary to have equal amounts of capacitive and inductive coupling, but in fact inductive coupling must dominate somewhat to compensate for the variation of unloaded Q with frequency. One example where the skewing of filter response can be used to advantage is in the design of a duplexer, which enables a transmitter and a receiver of slightly different frequency to operate simultaneously from a common antenna. Assume we are operating at VHF and the transmit frequency is higher than the receiving frequency (see Fig. 12). The receiving filter must provide enough attenuation at the transmitting frequency so that the receiving circuitry is not driven into compression or the transmitted signal does not generate undesired intermodulation distortion in the receiver. The transmitting filter must provide attenuation at the receiving frequency to prevent the transmitter's wideband noise from desensitizing the receiver and also to provide an impedance-match function that can be explained as follows: the more attenuation it presents at f_R, the smaller becomes the resistive component of its output impedance. Thus, at f_R the output impedance of the transmitting filter is almost pure reactive, which, when transformed by an appropriate length of transmission line l_T, appears as an open circuit at the receiving frequency. Therefore, as the receiving signal travels down the antenna, at the "T" junction it sees an open circuit toward the transmitting filter and a good match toward the receiving filter and, as a consequence, suffers no attenuation due to the presence of the alternate signal path. A similar argument holds for the receiving filter l_R, the transmitter to antenna insertion loss, and matching.

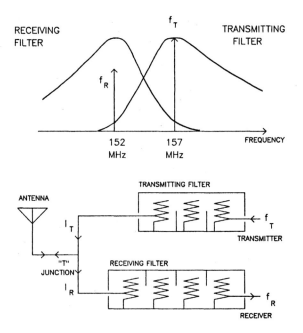

Fig. 12 Mobile Telephone Duplexer

It is clear that capacitive coupling should be used in the transmitting filter and inductive coupling in the receiving filter so that full advantage can be taken of the correct skewing of filter response to either provide further attenuation or decrease total number of resonators in implementing this duplexer. If inductive coupling is attempted, electric field between resonators should be shielded because coupling through E_r and H_r (two dominant components) is not in phase, possibly resulting in partial cancellation of coupling.

Chapter 3
Methods of Extending the Bandwidth

Given the constraints on geometry imposed by optimum Q-factor, helical resonators in a filter will be separated by a constant distance of $1.8d$ (circular shield) or $1.5d$ (square shield) as shown in Appendix I. The coupling apertures can then be enlarged to get a wider bandwidth up to a maximum, where the apertures are enlarged, eliminating the walls separating individual resonators from each other. At this point, the bandwidth of a helical filter will approach 10%. If it is desired to increase the bandwidth still further, or if some other factors prevent enlarging the apertures, several solutions are available and will be presented in this chapter.

In Chapter 2 it was found that the radial electric field was the strongest component and, in most cases, represented the dominant coupling mechanism. In attempting to increase the coupling between resonators, it is logical to exploit this dominance of the radial electric field still further, rather than concentrate on any other field component. Thus, the task of increasing the bandwidth of helical filters reduces to the problem of increasing the radial electric field or increasing the mutual capacitance between adjacent resonators. The price one has to pay for this heavy capacitive coupling is a pronounced variation of bandwidth and unloaded Q with center frequency, as well as marked skewing of filter response on the low-frequency side.

A common way of increasing the capacitance between two conductors is simply to move them closer together. The same applies for helical resonator coupling. In fact, any multiresonator filter could be constructed without any apertures whatsoever, the coupling entirely controlled by the spacing between adjacent resonators [23]. The drawback of this method is that the unloaded Q is degraded, and also variable spacing between resonators is not always desirable from a manufacturing point of view. If degradation of unloaded Q cannot be tolerated, increased coupling can be achieved by flaring out the tops of the resonators (helix diameter increasing toward open-circuited end), an arrangement resulting in other advantages, as will be shown in Chapter 5. In applications where it is desired to keep the distance between resonators constant, increased coupling can be achieved by the use of a suitable dielectric as the coupling medium between resonators [24], illustrated in Fig. 13.

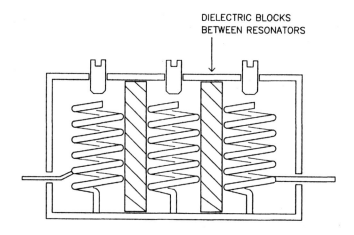

Fig. 13 Filter with Dielectric Apertures

With the use of thermally stable dielectrics such as alumina, polypropylene, and teflon, the bandwidth of helical filters can be extended to greater than 15% without any sacrifice in temperature performance. This method can also be used to increase the bandwidth of an existing filter with minimum effort. Figure 14 illustrates an application where, merely by inserting blocks of polypropylene dielectric into existing apertures, the bandwidth of a filter is in-

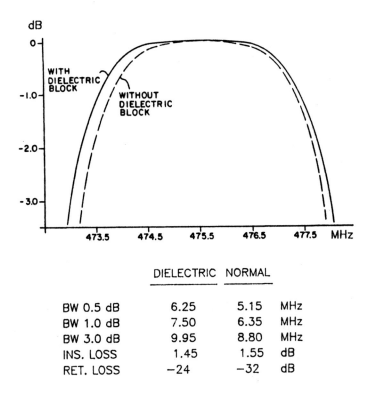

	DIELECTRIC	NORMAL	
BW 0.5 dB	6.25	5.15	MHz
BW 1.0 dB	7.50	6.35	MHz
BW 3.0 dB	9.95	8.80	MHz
INS. LOSS	1.45	1.55	dB
RET. LOSS	−24	−32	dB

Fig. 14 Dielectric Used as Coupling Medium

creased by more than one MHz. The return loss was slightly de-graded, because the input-output taps were not adjusted for increased loading.

Still greater bandwidths can be obtained by judiciously placing a coupling loop (in the shape of an inverted *U*) between two adjacent resonators near the ungrounded end [25] as shown in Fig. 15. (This can almost be considered as connecting a small discrete capacitor between resonator tops.) The position, width, height, thickness, and degree to which the sides are parallel are all parameters which markedly affect the coupling and thus the bandwidth. In addition, any dielectric (such as glue or epoxy) used to secure the loop in place also affects the coupling.

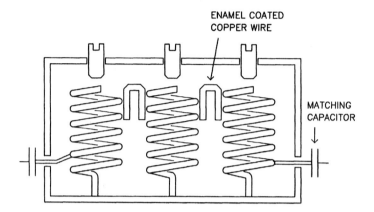

Fig. 15 Filter with Coupling Loops

Figures 16 and 17 illustrate a three-resonator filter similar to that in Fig. 15, that covers a 54% bandwidth. Figure 16 shows the passband which no longer shows the Butterworth response due to the heavy coupling between resonators. Figure 17 shows a wideband sweep of the whole filter illustrating the skewing of filter response on the low-frequency side. The reresonance near three times the center frequency is also apparent and illustrates a problem that will be described in Chapter 7.

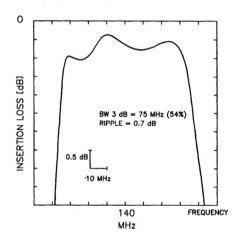

Fig. 16 Passband of a Wideband Filter

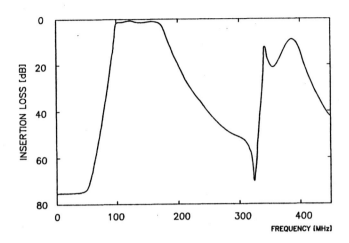

Fig. 17 Wideband Sweep of 54% BW Filter

A problem always encountered in the design of wideband helical filters is the difficulty of obtaining a sufficiently low loaded Q from the first and last resonator of the filter. Figure 18 illustrates the effect of moving the tap away from ground on the loaded Q. The vertical axis represents $\Delta 3$ dB, the frequency difference between 3 dB down points on the loaded Q curve (a measurement described in Chapter 1). When $\Delta 3$ dB is evaluated as a percentage of center frequency, the result is $1/Q_{loaded}$. Thus, from Fig. 18 it is clear that the loaded Q exhibits a minimum (i.e., $\Delta 3$ dB maximum) when the distance from the tap to the grounded end of the resonator represents approximately 13% of the total resonator length. What this means in practice is that with this tap placement a three-cell Butterworth filter can have a maximum bandwidth of under 13%, a four-cell under 10%, a five-cell under 8%, and a six-cell under 6.7%. If the bandwidth is increased beyond these amounts, the response will no longer be Butterworth, but will show over-coupled behavior (increased ripple in passband, pronounced ripple in return loss).

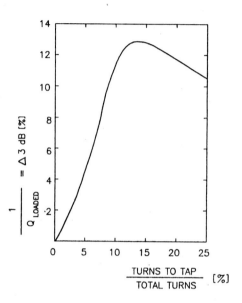

Fig. 18 Loaded Q as a Function of Tap Location

A solution to this surprising limitation can be obtained by viewing the problem from an impedance-match point of view: the increased coupling required for wider bandwidth represents an essentially capacitive load at the resonator top as previously described. This capacitive component is transformed by the quarter-wave length of the resonator itself into an inductive reactance appearing at the filter input. This inductive reactance can be tuned out by a series capacitor. Thus, if a capacitor of suitable value is placed in series with the input and output of an overcoupled filter, a good match to source and load can be obtained, reducing passband ripple and insertion loss. In fact, the capacitive coupling, resonator electrical length, and matching capacitance all vary with frequency in exactly the right manner to produce a very good impedance match across the passband of the filter.

Figure 19 shows how this series capacitor lowers the loaded Q of the first resonator and Figs. 20 and 21(a) illustrate how good an impedance match (high return loss) can be obtained using this technique. Figure 21(b) shows the input impedance of the same

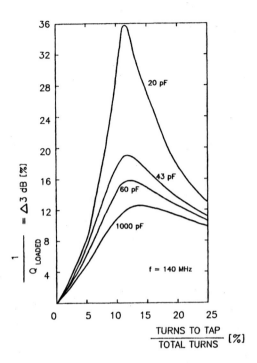

Fig. 19 Δ3 dB as a Function of Tap Location and Series Capacitor

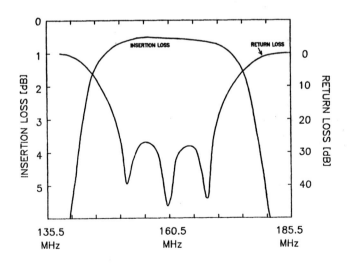

Fig. 20 Filter with Coupling Loops and Capacitor Matching

36

filter without series capacitors. In summary, two modifications are necessary to obtain wider bandwidth: increasing the coupling between adjacent resonators, and modifying the input and output impedance matching to obtain lower loaded Q.

IMPEDANCE OR ADMITTANCE COORDINATES

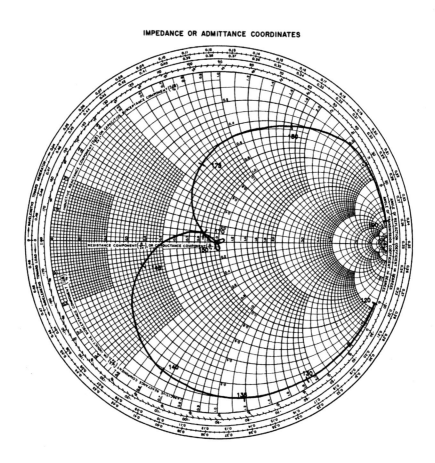

Fig. 21(a) Input Impedance of Filter of Fig. 20

37

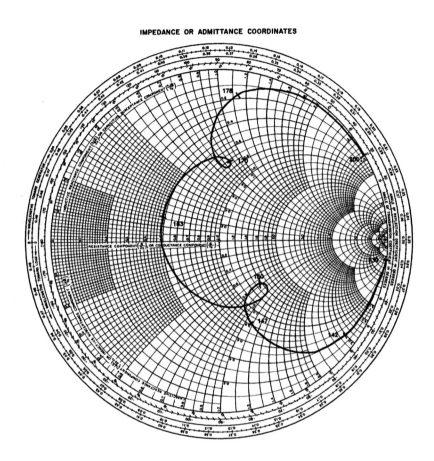

IMPEDANCE OR ADMITTANCE COORDINATES

Fig. 21(b) Filter of Fig. 20 without Matching Capacitors

Chapter 4
Variation of Filter Bandwidth with Center Frequency

In the design of tunable helical resonator filters, the variation of bandwidth with center frequency together with temperature stability present the two most serious problems encountered. Temperature stability demands a separate discussion and will be treated in Chapter 6, while in this section the problem of bandwidth variation with center frequency will be analyzed and a solution following from the field expressions will be presented.

Let us first examine the problem. Consider a tunable receiver employing helical resonator filters as shown in Fig. 22. The injection filter, apart from its obvious function of suppressing harmonics and subharmonics of the local oscillator (LO) source, has a much more subtle and important function. In reality, any LO source, whether it is a crystal oscillator, synthesizer, or LC oscillator will produce noise around the desired injection frequency (normally specified as single-sideband (SSB) *S/N* ratio in a particular bandwidth). Therefore, what the mixer ''sees'' are two signals as shown in Fig. 23.

Let us introduce some quantitative numbers into the above example. Suppose that the receiver sensitivity is specified as − 113 dBm (0.5 μV) RF level for 20 dB *S/N* ratio at IF. Further, assume that the mixer needs + 10 dBm injection level to operate and that the LO noise is found to be 90 dB down at $f_{LO} \pm f_{IF}$ when measured in the IF filter bandwidth. It is clear that without the injection filter

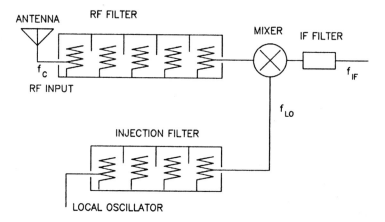

Fig. 22 Generalized Receiver Front End Schematic

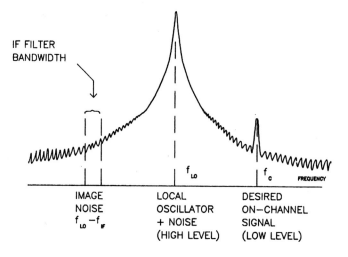

Fig. 23 Signals at Mixer Inputs

the receiver cannot meet the sensitivity specification because the on-channel and image noise from the local oscillator would be at -80 dBm, completely burying the desired signal at -113 dBm, assuming that the mixer does not reject some of this noise (this property depends on the mixer type). Therefore, the injection filter has to provide at least 53 dB attenuation (113 + 20 − 80) at the on-channel and image frequencies for the receiver to meet the sensitivity specification.

The function of the RF filter is to protect the mixer from spurious signals at frequencies other than f_c. The two worst spurious frequencies for low-side injection occur at $f_c - 2 \times f_{IF}$ (image frequency) and $f_c - f_{IF}/2$ (called the "half-IF spur," it is a second-order effect which arises from the product of twice the input frequency and twice the LO frequency).

The mixer has no protection for the image frequency (unless an expensive image-rejection mixer is used), while offering some degree of protection for the half-IF spur, which is very dependent on mixer type. Therefore, the RF filter must provide all the attenuation at the image frequency and some attenuation at the half-IF spur frequency. In addition, it must also provide some fixed rejection at the LO frequency, to keep receiver radiation within prescribed limits. The various frequency relationships are shown in Fig. 24.

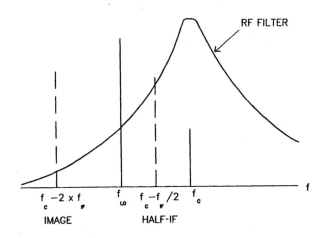

Fig. 24 Two Worst Spurious Frequencies Shown as Dotted Lines

What happens as both filters are tuned from one end of their tuning range to the other? At the low end, the bandwidth of both filters cannot be made arbitrarily narrow because of insertion loss considerations and thus is fixed at some minimum value. As the filters are tuned up in frequency, the bandwidth increases and, as a consequence, the spurious frequency rejection of RF filter and noise rejection of injection filter degrade often to the point of not meeting required specifications. Further addition of resonators to improve selectivity at the high-frequency end increases insertion loss at the low-frequency end of the tuning range. It frequently happens that while individual resonators are perfectly capable of covering the required tuning range, they can only be used in part of it because of excessive variation of bandwidth with center frequency. The tuning range then has to be split into several bands, and filter characteristics (number of turns on coil, aperture size, *etcetera*) have to change from band to band. This clearly represents an inefficient use of helical resonators in view of their broad tuning range capability.

Why does the bandwidth change with frequency? In the analysis below, it will be shown that for narrow bandwidth filters, the relative (percentage) bandwidth stays constant, an observation that can be verified by experiment. This, of course, means that as the center frequency is increased, the bandwidth increases in the same proportion. Since the IF stays constant, this represents a degradation of performance. For wide bandwidth filters, even the percentage bandwidth increases with frequency and can be attributed to excessive variation of unloaded Q with frequency as mentioned in Chapter 3.

Before going back to the field expressions in analyzing this situation, a few remarks about unloaded Q are in order. In [13] an expression for Q of the form $Q_{\text{UNLOADED}} = 44bf^{1/2}$ (see 2.25) can be found, implying a square-root dependence on frequency. One should keep in mind that this expression for unloaded Q is applicable only to ideal resonators with optimum dimensions. As soon as a tuning mechanism is introduced, or optimal geometry is disturbed by a wide aperture or by other means of extending the bandwidth, the dependence of unloaded Q on frequency changes markedly. In the case of a tuning screw disturbing the optimal geometry, the dependence of Q on frequency is almost linear, as shown in Fig. 25.

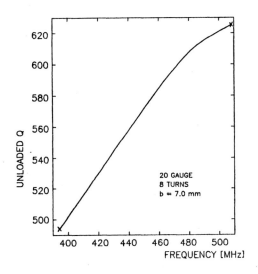

Fig. 25 Unloaded Q in a Copper Cavity

Therefore, let us examine what happens when the factor A in the field expressions is allowed to vary linearly with frequency. Equation (2.20) for the propagation constant can be considerably simplified for $b/a = 1.82$ (optimum Q) and in the neighborhood of $\gamma a = 0.2$:

$$\beta_0 a \cot \psi = 1.3\gamma a, \qquad 0.1 < \gamma a < 0.3 \tag{4.1}$$

Using this relationship, (2.1) to (2.19) can be evaluated exactly for the VHF resonator used in Chapter 2, and the influence of changing β_0 (changing frequency) on the field components can be determined. Let us take two resonant frequencies, 152 MHz and 170 MHz, solve (4.1) for the radial propagation constant and evaluate all 12 field components for the two frequencies (see Table 4).

44

Table 4

	$f_0 = 170$ MHz, $\omega_0 = 1.068 \times 10^9$ rad/s $\gamma a = 0.2574$ $\gamma = 78$	$f_0 = 152$ MHz, $\omega_0 = 9.55 \times 10^8$ rad/s $\gamma a = 0.231$ $\gamma = 70$ constant A	A changes linearly with frequency
(a) Inside helix at $r = 0$			
	$E_z = A$	$E_z = A$	$E_z = A \times \dfrac{152}{170} = 0.89A$
	$E_r = 0$	$E_r = 0$	$E_r = 0$
	$E_\theta = 0$	$E_\theta = 0$	$E_\theta = 0$
	$H_z = -jA0.016$	$H_z = -jA0.018$	$H_z = -jA0.016$
	$H_r = 0$	$H_r = 0$	$H_r = 0$
	$H_\theta = 0$	$H_\theta = 0$	$H_\theta = 0$
(b) Outside helix at $r = 6.0 \times 10^{-3}$ m (at shield)			
	$E_z = 0$	$E_z = 0$	$E_z = 0$
	$E_r = -jA4.88$	$E_r = -jA5.48$	$E_r = -jA4.90$
	$E_\theta = 0$	$E_\theta = 0$	$E_\theta = 0$
	$H_z = jA6.9 \times 10^{-3}$	$H_z = jA7.65 \times 10^{-3}$	$H_z = jA6.8 \times 10^{-3}$
	$H_r = 0$	$H_r = 0$	$H_r = 0$
	$H_\theta = A5.9 \times 10^{-4}$	$H_\theta = A6.62 \times 10^{-4}$	$H_\theta = A5.9 \times 10^{-4}$

If *A* is allowed to change linearly with frequency in the field expressions, the following result is obtained: The fields outside the resonator remain constant with changing resonant frequency, confirming the observation that percentage bandwidth remains the same for narrow bandwidth filters (filters where aperture is small enough not to significantly affect the field configuration or *Q* variation).

Another remarkable result which follows from the data in Table 4 is that if the unloaded *Q* is not allowed to change with frequency (constant *A*) fields outside the resonator actually increase with decreasing frequency, thus approaching the desired result of increasing percentage bandwidth with decreasing frequency, a condition favorable for obtaining filters with constant absolute bandwidth.

In summary, if a resonator could be obtained whose unloaded *Q* remains constant with frequency, a filter of constant absolute bandwidth could be constructed. Because a constant Q resonator is difficult to obtain to verify this finding by experiment, a compromise had to be made in constructing a filter as shown in Fig. 26.

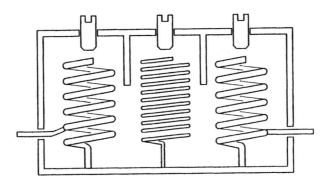

Fig. 26 Filter Using the Middle Coil in 3λ/4 Resonant Mode

The first and last coils were conventional λ/4 resonators dimensioned for optimum *Q* and tapped for the desired loaded *Q*. The middle coil, however, had three times as many turns and finer pitch, so that its 3λ/4 resonant frequency coincided with the λ/4 resonance of the other two resonators. The reason this was done is because the $3\lambda/4$ resonance exhibits a region of decreasing unloaded Q with increasing frequency for a particular position of the tuning screw, as shown in Fig. 27. Thus, it was hoped that the decreasing Q of the middle resonator would compensate for the increasing Q of the first and last resonators, and a constant bandwidth filter would be obtained. Figure 28 shows that the desired result was, indeed, obtained. A conventional filter would have changed bandwidth by 0.5 MHz in the frequency span shown in Fig. 28.

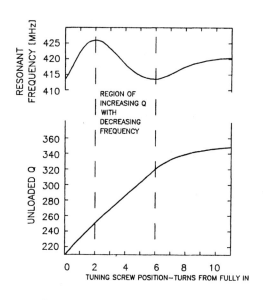

Fig. 27 Resonant Frequency and Q Variation with Tuning at $3\lambda/4$ Resonance

In concluding this chapter on variation of filter bandwidth with center frequency, a very good application of constant bandwidth filters follows for the case of varactor-tuned helical resonator filters. The problem of changing bandwidth is especially acute for this class of filters because, with varactor tuning, helical resonators can easily tune over an octave, which means that the corresponding filter bandwidth will also double in traversing this tuning range.

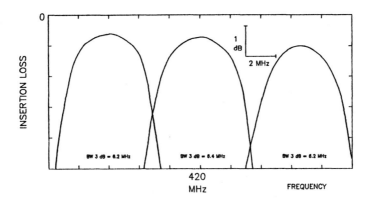

Fig. 28 Tunable Filter with Nearly Constant Bandwidth

Single varactor-tuned resonators, either half- or quarter-wave, have been studied, and optimum parameters with respect to tuning range and unloaded Q have been determined [19, 20]. Briefly, a varactor diode is connected from the point of voltage maximum (open end for $\lambda/4$, midpoint for $\lambda/2$ resonator) to ground. The varactor can be inside or outside the shield, or even running down the inside of the helix itself [21]. The capacitance is then varied by an external dc power supply. Conceptually, the mechanical capacitive tuning screw has been replaced by an electrically variable capacitance for the purpose of changing resonant frequency. The design of varactor-tuned resonators usually involves trade-offs between tuning range and varactor unloaded Q. Another important factor is the tracking of capacitance with voltage from diode to diode.

The varactor Q unfortunately changes in the same sense as the Q of a helical resonator—it generally decreases as frequency decreases (capacitance increases), with the result that the overall Q shows marked variation with frequency [19], especially for varactor Q less than resonator Q. This, of course, represents an undesirable characteristic for constant-bandwidth filter applications.

One solution to this problem is to introduce electrically variable coupling between resonators or to use a coupling network composed of discrete components designed to have the correct coupling coefficient variation with frequency [30]. Either method has disadvantages because the resonator geometry has to be disturbed by the placement of discrete components, dc returns and such, all of which potentially reduce the available Q, introduce spurious resonances, and make the filter difficult to construct. The most satisfactory solution follows from conclusions drawn earlier in this chapter: use a constant Q resonator, controlled by a hyperabrupt varactor of sufficiently high quality factor not to affect the overall unloaded Q.

Chapter 5
Tradeoffs Involving Unloaded Q-Factor

What improvement in filter performance can be obtained by increasing the unloaded Q-factor or, conversely, what effects will be apparent when the expected unloaded Q is not obtained? To answer these questions it should first be emphasized that the effects of unloaded Q on performance are not equal for all resonators in a filter. Resonators in the middle of a filter are loaded more lightly than those at the input or output. Consequently, the important quantity becomes $Q_{UNLOADED}/Q_{LOADED}$, where Q_{LOADED} for each resonator can be defined as its "working" or doubly-loaded Q and can be either calculated or measured by a previously described method. Consider a seven-resonator filter with f_0 = 500 MHz, BW 3 dB = 5 MHz. The loaded Q-factors are then as given in Table 5.

Table 5

Resonator No.:	1	2	3	4	5	6	7
Working Q:	22.3	62.3	90.1	100	90.1	62.3	22.3

From the example of Table 5, it is clear that the middle resonator has the highest loaded Q and, thus, is the most sensitive to any variation in its unloaded quality factor. In general, as the unloaded Q is increased, the insertion loss improves and can be traded off by adding more sections, thus achieving better selectivity. In the last chapter, we also saw that the unloaded Q varies approximately linearly with frequency and that increased Q results in wider bandwidth. Higher order filters, or very narrow filters, are easier to design with high Q resonators because the filter becomes physically symmetrical from input to output. Filters with low unloaded Q, on the other hand, do not have symmetrical coupling coefficients, and their input-output taps are different. A rule-of-thumb can be devised for separating these two classes of filters from each other as follows:

$$Q_{\text{UNLOADED}} \geqslant 10 \times Q_{\min} \qquad (5.1)$$

for which the filter is symmetrical, where

$$Q_{\min} = \left(\frac{f_0}{\text{BW 3 dB}}\right) q_n \qquad (5.2)$$

and q_n = normalized Q of first resonator (depends on total number of resonators; can be found in Zverev [3, p. 518]).

We can, therefore, summarize that it is always desirable to have as high an unloaded Q as possible. In practice, the constraints on unloaded Q are the available space for a filter, or perhaps the material that has to be used in constructing the resonators. At this point, let us review what is known about optimum Q resonators and whether it is possible to produce a resonator with unloaded Q even higher than the accepted optimum. The unloaded Q of a shielded helical resonator is thought to exceed the Q of an unshielded one because the proximity of the shield causes crowding of the current toward that side of wire closest to the shield [13]. As the shield is brought in from infinity, this proximity effect causes the radial electric field (which is the dominant component) to increase rapidly, thus increasing energy storage, while simultaneously decreasing helix losses. There is an optimum shield distance past which the shield losses start to dominate.

Let us now extend this idea still further as follows: The dominant loss mechanism is due to a current flowing through surface resistance of thickness δ (skin depth). This current could be produced by a source on the helix, or induced in the shield. From the field expressions of Chapter 2, we saw that most of this current flows near the grounded end of the helix. The top of the resonator, which carries much less current, nevertheless carries most of the stored energy, and it becomes doubtful to what extent the optimum *b/a* ratio derived from the current proximity effect is still valid in a region of minimal current flow.

Examining the relative magnitudes and phases of the electric and magnetic field components, it is clear that the instantaneous energy, rather than flowing from electric to magnetic field and back twice per cycle, is also transferred between the radial and longitudinal components of the electric field. Both of these components show a maximum at the open end of the helix. (The longitudinal field is zero at the shield, but is nonzero elsewhere, and dominates *inside* the helix.) Because there is very little current flowing near the ungrounded end of the resonator, the dominant effect on unloaded Q is just the amount of stored energy, which can be modeled to a first order as the product of the longitudinal electric field squared and the volume inside the helix, added to the product of the radial electric field component squared and the volume between the helix and the shield.

$$E_{stored} \propto \frac{1}{2}\epsilon_0 \int_0^a \left| E_z \text{ (inside helix)} \right|^2 2\pi r\, dr$$

$$+ \frac{1}{2}\epsilon_0 \int_a^b \left| E_r \text{ (outside helix)} \right|^2 2\pi r\, dr \qquad (5.3)$$

A solution of $\partial E_{stored}/\partial a = 0$ would likely yield a b/a ratio different from the value 1.82 given in Appendix I. This can be seen intuitively as follows: As the helix diameter increases, or as $a \rightarrow b$, the radial electric field outside the helix sharply increases due to the factor Δ_0 in (2.15), while the longitudinal electric field inside the helix remains approximately constant, or slightly increases proportional to the function $I_0 (\gamma r)$. At this point, the radial electric field between helix and shield is stronger, but is contained in a smaller volume so that these two effects even out each other. Essentially, as the helix diameter is increased slightly, the stored energy is not significantly affected. Equivalently, (5.3) does not show a very sharp peak. Increasing the helix diameter, however, increases the capacitance to the shield walls, which in turn lowers the resonant frequency. Finally, we reach the surprising conclusion that as the helix top is flared out, the resonant frequency decreases while the Q remains unaffected, defeating the $\sqrt{f_0}$ variation in Q predicted for a cylindrical resonator (2.25).

Let us continue the discussion to include the effect of a tuning screw that runs axially inside the helix (rather than outside the helix). Here the problem is that the tuning screw eliminates a substantial portion of the longitudinal electric field inside the helix, decreasing the stored energy. Again, as the helix diameter is increased (or tuning screw diameter is decreased), a similar trade-off becomes apparent, but now between a stronger longitudinal field and a weaker radial field (both inside helix) over a larger volume. In this case, however, as the helix diameter is increased, the resonant frequency *goes up* because the capacitance to the tuning screw dominates over the capacitance to shield and is decreased as the helix moves away from the tuning screw. All of these effects can be seen in Fig. 29, which shows the unloaded Q of a resonator that is flared out towards the top, compared to the unloaded Q of a conventional cylindrical resonator of optimum dimensions. The first characteristic immediately apparent is that an improvement in unloaded Q is obtained without any penalty in volume. The second item of interest is a decrease in tuning range explained previously by an interaction between the shield and tuning screw capacitances. The two endpoints of both curves (marked by X's) represent the tuning screw fully in (low-frequency end) and fully out (high-frequency end). In the fully-out position, the unloaded Q is approximately the same for both resonators, while the resonant frequency of the tapered resonator is lower, as previously described. The dimensions of this improved resonator are given in Fig. 30. In a given volume, maximum Q can be obtained when the helix top is flared out, while at the grounded end the b/a ratio (same as D/d or S/d) given in Appendix I should be maintained. This tapered

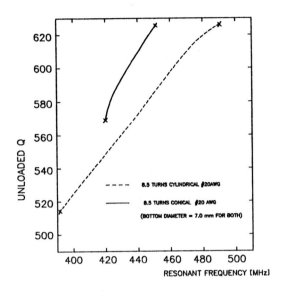

Fig. 29 Tapered Resonator

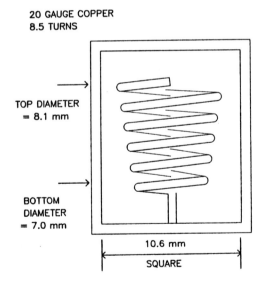

Fig. 30 Tapered Resonator

resonator yields unloaded Q that is about 5% higher than a conventional, cylindrical resonator but does so at the expense of reduced tuning range and increased manufacturing complexity (cost). A tapered resonator can be used to approximate a constant Q resonator. Consider a conventional cylindrical resonator without a tuning screw. A mechanical arrangement which increases the diameter of the top few turns would produce a constant Q resonator over a limited frequency range. This is because the resonator volume, which determines the Q, does not change, while the resonant frequency does.

Chapter 6
Temperature and Mechanical Stability

It is always desirable, and often necessary, to design filters with resonators having resonant frequency drift with temperature minimized. When the resonant frequency does change with temperature, the whole passband of the resultant filter moves up and down in frequency, with the predictable result that the insertion loss at the bandedge frequencies changes by an amount depending on filter bandwidth and construction. In addition, unloaded Q degrades with increasing temperature, further affecting the insertion loss and bandwidth. Generally, narrow bandwidth filters suffer more from temperature problems than wide bandwidth filters.

The key to understanding and solving the problem of resonant frequency drift with temperature lies in the observation that a resonator made of copper helix and enclosed in a copper shield (either square or circular cross section) without a tuning screw drifts very little in frequency with temperature. (It is important to note here that we are dealing with helical resonators applied to RF filters. If a helical resonator is used as a frequency-determining element in an oscillator, for example, even the slight frequency drift of this pure copper resonator may not be acceptable. In such a case, a tuning mechanism with custom-tailored thermal expansion coefficient should be designed and other considerations, such as cost or mechanical stability, would not be as important. For RF filtering applications, the aim is not to make the frequency drift zero, but only to decrease it to less than approximately 20 ppm/°C, which is sufficient for most filtering applications.) However, a resonator constructed as described has several problems: a helix supported only at the grounded end is not stable mechanically and will vibrate (change resonant frequency and unloaded Q) with shock. Also, a resonator with walls and apertures made of copper is expensive to produce. Finally, the resonator is not tunable.

Temperature stability is usually degraded by introducing features that solve these drawbacks. For example, winding the helix on a dielectric coil form for mechanical stability subjects the coil to the thermal expansion of the dielectric material itself. For the outside walls, using metal that can be cast easily, such as zinc or aluminum (which ensures repeatability of cavity and aperture sizes), again introduces a temperature coefficient of expansion different from copper, the material normally used for the helix. The tuning screw and the material of which it is made also affect the temperature stability of a resonator. The resonant frequency of a helical resonator shifts primarily because of a change of capacitance between the resonator top and its surroundings. Usually, the capacitance to the tuning screw dominates.

Let us now look at a few examples of resonator construction to gain further insight into factors affecting the resonant frequency shift. Table 6 presents a list of coefficients of linear thermal expansion (in kelvins, K) for several materials used in the following discussion:

Table 6

Copper	$16.7 \times 10^{-6} \text{ K}^{-1}$
Zinc	$30.0 \times 10^{-6} \text{ K}^{-1}$
Polypropylene	$100 \times 10^{-6} \text{ K}^{-1}$
Nickel	$12.6 \times 10^{-6} \text{ K}^{-1}$

Consider a resonator with an unsupported helix, copper (or brass) tuning screw, and a zinc shield. Because the linear expansion of zinc is almost twice that of copper, as the temperature is increased the shield will move away from the helix, taking the tuning screw with it, thus decreasing the capacitance to the helix top. This, in turn, increases the resonant frequency. The reverse would happen for a copper helix and nickel shield.

Next, consider the copper helix being wound or molded into a coil form made of polypropylene, enclosed in a copper shield. The expansion of the plastic would tend to lengthen the helix and increase its diameter beyond its natural expansion. However, the helix is much more rigid in the radial direction than longitudinal direction, and thus would increase in length to a greater degree than in diameter. Therefore, the capacitance to the tuning screw would increase with temperature (tuning screw would move *in* relative to the helix), and resonant frequency would decrease markedly due to the high expansion coefficient of polypropylene. Other dielectric materials that have a smaller coefficient of thermal expansion, such as rexolite, cross-linked polystyrene, or ceramics, could be used for the coil form, but these are costly and lack repeatability because these materials are not moldable and have to be machined to shape. One exception is polyphenylene sulphide, a moldable thermoplastic whose coefficient of thermal expansion is very close to that of zinc. Thus, a resonator constructed of a copper helix molded into polyphenylene sulphide, and enclosed in a zinc shield would show good thermal stability. The choice of material for the tuning screw presents one additional degree of freedom, and a suitable material could be chosen for further modification of the resonator temperature performance. For example, INVAR could be used with this combination to take advantage of its good dimensional stability.

In low-frequency resonators, which have to be wound with fine gauge wire, the expansion of the coil form material completely dominates, and the coil expands radially as well as longitudinally to the same extent as the plastic. In this case, the result is two opposing tendencies because longitudinal expansion decreases the resonant frequency, while radial expansion moves the helix away from the tuning screw and increases the resonant frequency. Therefore, changing the tuning screw diameter is all that is necessary to compensate for the thermal expansion of the rest of the resonator, regardless of its material. In general, the larger the diameter of the tuning screw, the more important the radial expansion becomes so that if the resonant frequency decreases with rising temperature, the tuning screw size should be increased and *vice versa*.

In high-frequency resonators constructed of heavy gauge wire on a dielectric coil form, radial expansion of the helix is restricted, as previously mentioned, so that there are no opposing frequency drifts which could be played against each other. However, it turns out that the longitudinal expansion of the coil form material usually completely dominates any other effect because the helix has very low longitudinal structural rigidity; it is essentially a spring expanded or contracted in length by the coil form material. Thus, it becomes of primary importance to limit the longitudinal expansion of the helix near its ungrounded end, for mechanical stability as well as for temperature effects. This can be accomplished by physically attaching the coil form to the top of the cavity, leaving the other end free to expand and contract (in this case it might be necessary to solder the helix ground to the side wall rather than cavity bottom). If it is not possible to leave the grounded side free to expand and contract, a substantial portion of coil form material might have to be removed part way down the coil between two adjacent turns to take up the thermal expansion [26]. Another method of securing the helix top against expansion is to thread the tuning screw into the coil form. Figure 31 shows a comparison between two resonators: one was constructed using a copper helix molded into a cylindrical polypropylene coil form; the other one was identical, except it had torque ribs on the inside of the coil form so that the tuning screw could thread into it. This feature decreased the frequency shift to less than a third of the initial change. This configuration, where the tuning screw threads into the dielectric coil form, also makes the structure very rigid and much less prone to mechanical and vibrational disturbances.

If it is desired to look at the frequency shift from a quantitative rather than qualitative point of view, the capacitance between the tuning screw and helix can be estimated as

$$C = \frac{2\pi \epsilon l}{\ln (b/a)} \tag{6.1}$$

where

  b = mean helix radius

  a = mean tuning screw radius

  ϵ = permittivity of medium

  l = distance that tuning screw penetrates into helix

Then, all the lengths and dielectric constant can be recalculated for a certain temperature change using the appropriate temperature coefficients, and a new capacitance can be estimated. Assuming that the resonant frequency changes as $1/\sqrt{C}$, the corresponding frequency change can be obtained. The difficulty here lies in estimating the expansion coefficient for two materials in direct contact, such as the helix and coil form on which it is wound. The two limiting cases for thin wire and heavy gauge wire have already been mentioned.

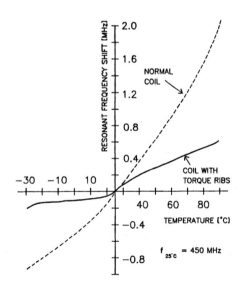

Fig. 31 Temperature Compensated Resonator

In summary, the frequency drift with temperature of a helical resonator can be minimized by a combination of tuning screw size and mechanical rigidity of helix top with respect to the tuning mechanism, depending on frequency of operation and materials used in constructing the resonator. Mechanical and vibrational stability considerations also dictate a lack of relative movement between resonator top and the tuning screw.

Chapter 7
Harmonic Reresonances
and Folded Resonators

A section of uniform helical or coaxial transmission line, short circuited at one end and open circuited at the other, will behave as a resonator at a frequency for which its electrical length is $\lambda/4$. At this frequency a standing wave can be supported such that the electric field at the open end and the magnetic field at the short-circuited end will show a maximum. This type of resonant behavior also occurs when the transmission line electrical length is

$$\frac{3\lambda}{4}, \frac{5\lambda}{4}, \cdots, \frac{(2n + 1)\lambda}{4}, \qquad n = 1, 2, \cdots$$

The higher order harmonics are eventually damped out by dielectric losses and higher order modes which do not necessarily show the right field distribution for supporting a standing wave at odd multiples of the fundamental $\lambda/4$ resonance. Higher order modes are introduced at both the shorted and open ends because these points represent discontinuities in the basic helical or coaxial structure having dimensions which are no longer small with respect to wavelength at high frequencies. It is to be expected, then, that a filter constructed of such resonators will also show multiple passbands with insertion loss steadily increasing with frequency. Figure 32 shows a VHF filter intended to operate at 139 MHz and Fig. 33 shows a UHF filter at 450 MHz with their respective reresonances.

62

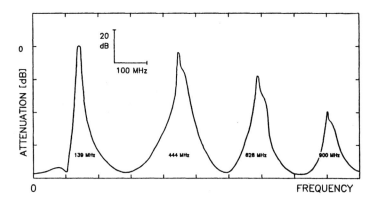

Fig. 32 VHF Filter and its Reresonances

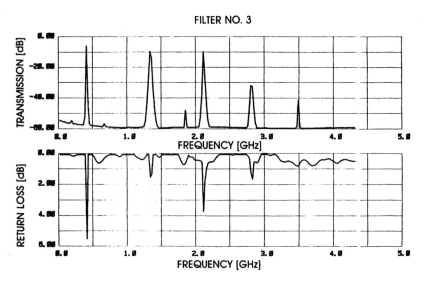

Fig. 33 UHF Filter and its Reresonances

The bandwidth of a filter at its reresonant frequencies can be wider or narrower, depending on aperture size and location, but is usually wider because the location of an electric or magnetic field maximum is more likely to be exposed to the aperture at the reresonant frequencies.

Let us examine the graph of Fig. 32 in more detail. The first characteristic that is immediately apparent is that the 3λ/4 reresonance peak does not occur exactly at three times the fundamental frequency. This is because the resonator walls and tuning screw present differing amounts of capacitive loading at the two frequencies, and thus affect the resonant frequencies differently. In fact, it is possible to *increase* the 3λ/4 resonant frequency by moving the tuning screw *in* for some position of the tuning screw, whereas the fundamental resonant frequency is always *decreased* by moving the tuning screw in. This can be explained as follows: Consider the field distribution of the electric and magnetic fields along the resonator (see Fig. 34). As the tuning screw is moved into the 3λ/4 resonator, its resonant frequency initially decreases because of increased end capacitance. This, in effect, moves the point of electric field phase reversal (point A) away from the grounded end. When the tuning screw moves in past the point of phase reversal, several effects become apparent. First, the tuning screw, made of solid metal (as opposed to being conductive only in a specific direction like the helix) is not long enough to support electric field reversal in such a short distance along its surface. Therefore, some of the electric field on the helix beyond the phase reversal point (towards grounded end) is canceled by induced electric field of opposite phase already present on the tuning screw. This interaction effectively moves the phase reversal point towards ground, thus decreasing the wavelength, which, of course, increases the resonant frequency. If the tuning screw goes in far enough, the electric field beyond the phase reversal point will begin to dominate, reverting the tuning mechanism back to its initial mode of operation. In this manner we can explain the graph of Fig. 27 presented in Chapter 4 where the resonant frequency of a 3λ/4 resonator, in contrast to its unloaded Q, does not show a monotonic change with tuning screw position. The unloaded Q, of course, decreases as the tuning screw is moved in because the stored energy is decreased and surface area is increased as mentioned previously in Chapter 5.

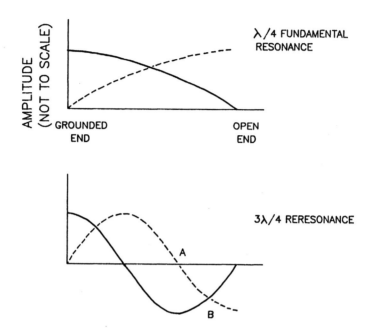

Fig. 34 Field Distribution along Helical or Coaxial Resonator
– – – electric field
_____ magnetic field

From the preceding discussion we can conclude that the frequency of the 3λ/4 reresonance is not necessarily exactly three times the λ/4 fundamental resonant frequency because of these different capacitance effects. This can also help explain why the passbands of the reresonances are not symmetrical or Butterworth in shape: the tuning screw positions that make the passband Butterworth at λ/4 resonance do not necessarily present the right capacitance for this kind of shape at the reresonant frequencies. Note also the progressive increase in insertion loss of the passbands and (see Fig. 32) the fact that the reresonant responses are not skewed to the same extent as the fundamental and are generally wider.

In a majority of applications, these reresonant responses are not desired and must somehow be suppressed. The simplest example of why these reresonances are a problem in a receiver can be illustrated using the circuit configuration of Chapter 4, shown again in Fig. 35. Let the RF filter be constructed using helical resonators; the injection filter construction is not important.

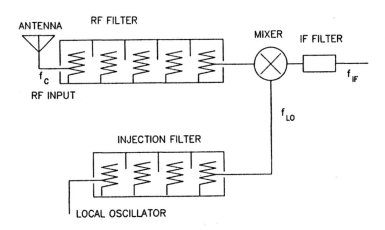

Fig. 35 Typical RF Receiver Front End

Harmonics of the LO frequency are generated in the mixer because, by definition, it is a nonlinear device. The relative level of these harmonics depends on the mixer type; for example, even-order harmonics are suppressed in double balanced mixers. Let us concentrate on the third harmonic which is generated at some level in the mixer, regardless of its type. This means that the mixer will respond to input frequencies at $3 \times f_{LO} \pm f_{IF}$ to give an output at the IF. However, we know that the RF filter shows a reresonant response near $3 \times f_c$, and thus is likely to pass the signal at $3 \times f_{LO} + f_{IF}$ for low-side injection or $3 \times f_{LO} - f_{IF}$ for high-side injection with only a few decibels of attenuation. Thus, our receiver has a problem with spurious responses at the frequencies $n \times f_{LO} \pm f_{IF}$, for $n \geqslant 3$ odd.

Assuming that the third harmonic level generated in the mixer is 15 dB down and that the input RF filter provides 10 dB attenuation at the $3 \times f_{LO} + f_{IF}$ frequency, the spurious response rejection would be approximately 25 dB, a far cry from the 70 dB required, for example, by the Department of Communications (Canada) or the 85 dB by the Federal Communication Commission (US) for land mobile receivers. Because of the reresonant responses, helical resonator filters cannot be used as transmitter harmonic filters and claims made by duplexer manufacturers that their device decreases transmitter harmonic output should be viewed with caution because this statement is true only for even harmonics.

The simplest solution to this reresonance problem conceptually is to add a low-pass filter in series with the helical filter because the reresonances are quite far away in frequency and can be easily attenuated in this manner. The drawbacks of this solution are that additional space is necessary for the low-pass filter and increased insertion loss necessary in the signal path.

Next, we will discuss methods that do not require the use of a low-pass filter, but involve modifying the resonators in some way. At this point we should make an important distinction regarding the electromagnetic field components as they relate to reresonance suppression. In approaching this problem, we are not seeking a helical structure that *suppresses propagation* in a certain frequency range; rather, we are merely seeking a structure that will not support *standing waves* in that region because it is the formation of a standing wave that represents resonance. One method of reresonance suppression involves changing the pitch of successive resonators in a filter. This method is part of a general approach to the problem, whereby the reresonant frequencies of the resonators in a filter are arranged to be different from each other, whether it is by different capacitive loading, changing the pitch, helix diameter, cavity size and shape, or some other method that ensures a slightly different reresonance frequency for each or some of the resonators, while keeping the fundamental $\lambda/4$ resonances still the same (with some degradation of unloaded Q). As a consequence, rather than showing a single passband, the reresonant response of the filter will consist of several peaks up to a maximum equal to the number of resonators in the filter. In this way, the reresonance will be suppressed by a certain amount (typically 20–30 dB), but it will also be spread out in frequency to a wider extent than the usual reresonance. Very often, the reresonance suppression achieved in this manner is not sufficient, especially for high-performance receivers, where a specification for spurious response rejection of 100 dB is not uncommon.

If it is desired to suppress the $3\lambda/4$ reresonance only by a small amount without sacrificing unloaded Q or adding an external low-pass filter, it can sometimes be accomplished by a judicious placement of the coupling aperture. For example, if it can be determined that E_r is still dominant at three times fundamental frequency (response still skewed on low-frequency side), then placing the aperture so that it is symmetrical about the point of electric field phase reversal (point A in Fig. 34) will result in two coupling modes, both equal but opposite in phase so that the contribution from E_r to coupling at the reresonance is canceled. If, however, electric field dominance cannot be assumed (reresonance is symmetrical and displays no skewing), then one could rely on the fact that E_r and H_z are of opposite phase as shown by (2.15) and (2.17). Thus an aperture that is symmetrical about point B of Fig. 34 could be used to cancel equal contributions from E_r and H_z and decrease coupling at the reresonance. It should be kept in mind that both points A and B move with tuning so that the success of this method of reresonance suppression greatly depends on the actual application of the final filter.

Another general approach to the reresonance problem is to use at least one resonator in a filter chain which shows even-order reresonances rather than odd-order [28]. With this arrangement, the resonators suppress each others' reresonances, thus achieving the desired result. A half-wave resonator will not perform the required function because it is just two $\lambda/4$ resonators in series and can certainly support all the field configurations of a $\lambda/4$ resonator, including the $3\lambda/4$ reresonance (which is its own $3\lambda/2$ resonance and is allowed). This approach is quite true of a coaxial resonator and partially true of a helical resonator. The helical resonator has one additional variable which alters its characteristics from those of a coaxial resonator, the pitch angle of the helix which can have values continuously variable from positive to negative numbers.

From the field expressions of Chapter 2 we see that radial electric field is normally the dominant coupling mechanism of helical resonator filters and (2.8) and (2.15) show that E_r is independent of the pitch angle ψ. Thus, it is not necessary for all resonators in a filter to have the same pitch or even the same sign of the pitch angle. Reverse pitch helices would work just as well and it would be impossible to determine whether the resonators were positive pitch, reverse pitch, or a mixture of the two from the filter's electrical characteristics. The pitch angle does matter a great deal, however, if it changes value or sign on the same resonator because half of the field expressions depend on the pitch angle, and if it reverses sign, six field components reverse their phase.

Let us examine a resonator that reverses pitch angle part way up the helix, with a short length of reverse pitch helix l_2 attached to the top of a longer section of normal pitch l_1 [29], as shown in Fig. 36. This type of structure will be called a folded resonator because the wire of which it is wound has to fold back on itself to create a winding of reverse pitch. When the fundamental resonant frequency of such a resonator is measured, it is found that it corresponds to $\lambda/4 = l_1 + l_2$ rather than $\lambda/4 = l_1$. The reresonance, however, is remarkably sensitive to the length l_2 relative to length l_1, and near $l_2/l_1 = 1/3$ the folded resonator approaches a reresonance that is four times the fundamental. Figure 37 shows an approximate relationship derived experimentally between l_2/l_1 and the multiplication factor (reresonance ratio) that relates the first reresonance to the fundamental $\lambda/4$ resonance. The graph of Fig. 37 is approximate in the sense that as the resonator is tuned, the tuning capacitance presented to the fundamental and first reresonance is different, thus changing the ratio n up to ± 0.5, depending on the tuning mechanism.

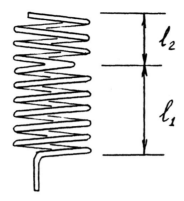

Fig. 36 Folded Resonator

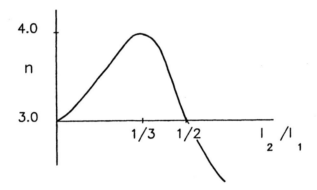

Fig. 37 Reresonance Ratio $n = f_{\text{RERESONANCE}}/f_{\text{FUNDAMENTAL}}$ as a Function of Length of Reverse Pitch on a Folded Resonator

Let us examine why the first reresonance frequency is so sensitive to the length of reverse pitch helix. Let us make only one assumption, that current must be continuous at the junction of opposite pitch windings. From this it immediately follows that the strength of the two dominant magnetic field components H_r and H_z will depend on length l_2 because current flowing on the reverse pitch helix will produce H_z and H_r components that are of opposite sign to those produced by current on l_1. Let us determine qualitatively what happens when the length l_2 is increased and what effect this will have on the cancellation of magnetic field components at some point on the helix. Summarizing Fig. 38, it is clear that as the length l_2 is increased, the reresonant frequency initially rises, then returns to its starting value and then drops even lower. Between cases (b) and (c) this reresonance frequency reaches a maximum which from experimental results is near $\frac{4}{3} f_R$ and happens at approximately $l_2/l_1 = \frac{1}{3}$.

Figure 39 shows a filter constructed with $l_1 = 21\frac{1}{2}$ turns and $l_2 = 7\frac{1}{2}$ turns ($l_2/l_1 = 0.35$), which results in a reresonance ratio:

$$n = \frac{f_{\text{RERESONANCE}}}{f_{\text{FUNDAMENTAL}}} = 3.9$$

This filter shows greater than 70 dB attenuation of signals near $3 \times f_{\text{FUNDAMENTAL}}$.

Figure 40 shows a filter with resonators of the previous type alternating with resonators of uniform pitch. This filter shows both $3 \times f_{\text{FUNDAMENTAL}}$ and $4 \times f_{\text{FUNDAMENTAL}}$ reresonances suppressed by 30 dB and 36 dB, respectively. Then arises the question of what level of reresonance suppression ultimately can be achieved by alternating resonators of odd and even reresonances. This number can be estimated by taking a normal three-cell filter constructed of uniform pitch helices, removing the center helix, and measuring what level of coupling is obtained between the first and third resonators. This arrangement simulates the case where the middle resonator is not resonant at the frequency of interest, but still supports the coupling fields generated between first and last resonators. The level of reresonance suppression measured with this arrangement depends on aperture dimensions, and is typically from 30 dB to 50 dB. From this we can conclude that, in general, it is better to use all folded resonators in a filter to place the reresonance in a frequency range where it cannot cause problems, rather than to rely on the even-odd suppression of alternating folded and uniform pitch resonators.

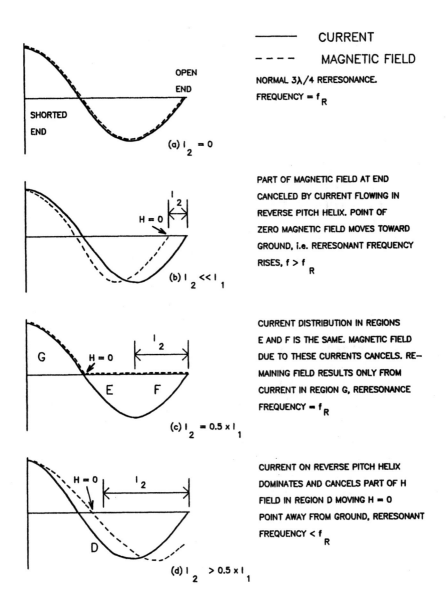

Fig. 38 Standing Wave Configuration as a Function of l_2/l_1

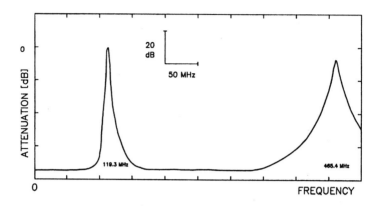

Fig. 39 Filter with Reresonance Ratio $n = 4$

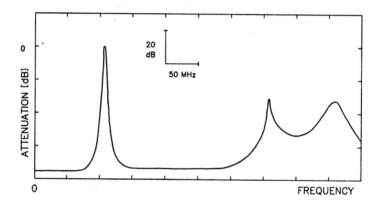

Fig. 40 Filter with Alternating $n = 3$ and $n = 4$ Resonators

Two final questions regarding the fundamental resonance remain to be answered in this section. Why is the fundamental $\lambda/4$ resonance not affected by changing l_2, and what is the impact on unloaded Q of introducing a section of reverse pitch helix? The first question can be answered as follows: For $l_2 \ll \lambda/4$, the presence of a length of reverse pitch helix does, indeed, shorten the electrical length, but at the same time presents a capacitive load at the end, so that the resonant frequency remains approximately constant because these two effects have opposite influence on the resonant frequency. As l_2 further increases, the decrease in electrical length will begin to dominate and the resonant frequency will tend to increase.

With this last argument we can tackle the second question regarding unloaded Q. Again, for $l_2 \ll \lambda/4$ the unloaded Q will remain unaffected, but as soon as the resonant frequency starts to increase, this immediately means a reduction in unloaded Q. The argument goes as follows: Consider a uniform pitch helix, and a folded resonator wound with the same length of wire and l_2 large enough to raise the resonant frequency. These two resonators will have approximately the same unloaded Q (because they are wound with the same length of wire, and the proximity effect on which the unloaded Q depends is independent of the sign of the pitch angle). What this means is that if it is desired to make the two resonant frequencies the same, more turns have to be added to the folded resonator which, of course, means that Q is degraded. The converse of this argument was illustrated in Chapter 5, where by flaring out the resonator top we achieved a lower resonant frequency without having to increase the number of turns (length of wire), thus maintaining the same unloaded Q at the lowered resonant frequency (see Fig. 29), which represents an improvement over the usual cylindrical resonator.

Figure 41 shows a comparison of two folded resonators with a uniform pitch resonator. For $l_2/l_1 = 0.36$ this decrease in unloaded Q is clearly evident. For $l_2/l_1 = 0.15$ the graph shows an improvement in unloaded Q which can be explained by an observation that, in constructing this folded resonator, length l_2 of reverse pitch was inadvertently made of slightly larger diameter than l_1 (approximately 5% larger), further illustrating the effect presented in Chapter 5. Thus, folded resonators present a method of dealing with undesired reresonances without significantly compromising unloaded Q.

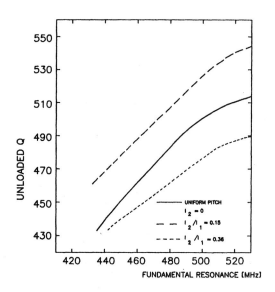

Fig. 41 Unloaded Q as a Function of Frequency with l_2/l_1 as a Parameter

Appendix I
Optimum Conventional Resonator

I.1 PROPORTIONS OF AN OPTIMAL CONVENTIONAL HELICAL RESONATOR [1–3]

Resonator is optimal in the sense of giving the highest unloaded Q for the specified cylindrical helix diameter to shield distance and wire size to pitch ratios. Figure 42 shows a shield of circular cross section; Figure 43 shows a shield of square cross section.

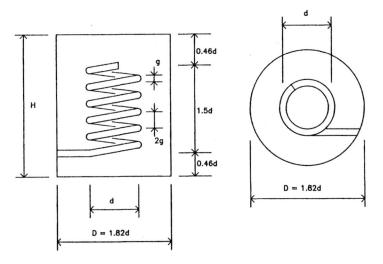

Fig. 42 Shield of Circular Cross Section

76

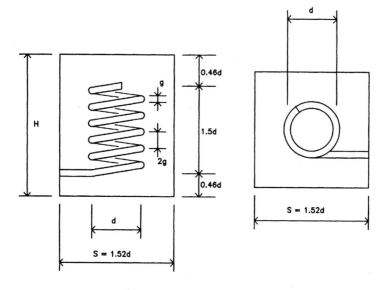

Fig. 43 Shield of Square Cross Section

Appendix II
Field Derivation

II.1 THE ELECTROMAGNETIC FIELD OF A SHEATH HELIX IN FREE SPACE SURROUNDED BY A CONCENTRIC CONDUCTIVE CYLINDER DERIVED FROM FIRST PRINCIPLES

From cylindrical symmetry (Fig. 44), assume fields are of the form:

$$E_z = [AI_0(\gamma r) + BK_0(\gamma r)]e^{j(\omega t - \beta z)}$$
$$H_z = [CI_0(\gamma r) + DK_0(\gamma r)]e^{j(\omega t - \beta z)}$$

where

E_z = longitudinal component of electric field
H_z = longitudinal component of magnetic field
I_0 = modified Bessel function of first kind, order zero
K_0 = modified Bessel function of second kind, order zero
A,B,C,D = constants determined by boundary conditions

Also assume the following:

- there is no θ variation of the fields, $\partial/\partial\theta = 0$
- neglect attenuation: $\gamma^2 = \beta^2 - \beta_0^2$

77

78

β = propagation constant inside helix

β₀ = free space propagation constant

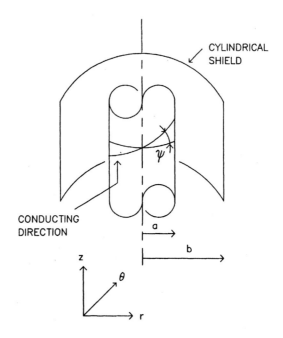

Fig. 44 Sheath Helix Surrounded by a Concentric Conductive Cylinder

II.1.1 Maxwell's Equations in Cylindrical Coordinates

Starting from $\nabla \times \overline{H} = j\omega\,\epsilon\overline{E}$ and noting that $\partial/\partial\theta = 0$, $\partial/\partial z = -j\beta$,

$$\hat{r}(j\beta H_\theta) + \hat{\theta}\left(-j\beta H_r - \frac{\partial H_z}{\partial r}\right) + \hat{z}\left[\frac{1}{r}\frac{\partial}{\partial r}(rH_\theta)\right]$$

$$= j\omega\epsilon\,(\hat{r}E_r + \hat{\theta}E_\theta + \hat{z}E_z)$$

Equating the components we obtain

$$E_r = \frac{\beta}{\omega\epsilon}H_\theta$$

$$E_\theta = -\frac{\beta}{\omega\epsilon}H_r - \frac{1}{j\omega\epsilon}\frac{\partial H_z}{\partial r}$$

By a similar procedure starting with $\nabla \times \overline{E} = -j\omega\mu\,\overline{H}$, we obtain

$$H_r = -\frac{\beta}{\omega\mu}E_\theta$$

$$H_\theta = \frac{\beta}{\omega\mu}E_r + \frac{1}{j\omega\mu}\frac{\partial E_z}{\partial r}$$

Expressing all the components in terms of E_z and H_z, we obtain

$$H_\theta = \frac{j\omega\epsilon}{\gamma^2}\frac{\partial E_z}{\partial r}$$

$$E_r = \frac{j\beta}{\gamma^2}\frac{\partial E_z}{\partial r}$$

$$H_r = \frac{j\beta}{\gamma^2}\frac{\partial H_z}{\partial r}$$

$$E_\theta = -\frac{j\omega\mu}{\gamma^2}\frac{\partial H_z}{\partial r}$$

II.1.2   Field Components Inside Helix

Assume only finite fields exist, and there are no terms in $K_0(\gamma r)$.

Also note that

$$\frac{\partial I_0(\gamma r)}{\partial r} = \gamma I_1(\gamma r)$$

$$E_z^i = A^i I_0(\gamma r) e^{j(\omega t - \beta z)}$$

$$H_z^i = C^i I_0(\gamma r) e^{j(\omega t - \beta z)}$$

where A^i, C^i = constants to be determined, superscript stands for "inside". Expressing the other components in terms of E_z^i and H_z^i, we obtain

$$E_r^i = \frac{j\beta}{\gamma} A^i I_1(\gamma r) e^{j(\omega t - \beta z)}$$

$$E_\theta^i = -\frac{j\omega\mu}{\gamma} C^i I_1(\gamma r) e^{j(\omega t - \beta z)}$$

$$H_r^i = \frac{j\beta}{\gamma} C^i I_1(\gamma r) e^{j(\omega t - \beta z)}$$

$$H_\theta^i = \frac{j\omega\epsilon}{\gamma} A^i I_1(\gamma r) e^{j(\omega t - \beta z)}$$

II.1.3 Field Components Outside Helix

Both I_0 and K_0 terms are allowed:

$$\frac{\partial K_0(\gamma r)}{\partial r} = -\gamma K_1(\gamma r)$$

$$E_z^0 = [A^0 I_0(\gamma r) + B^0 K_0(\gamma r)] e^{j(\omega t - \beta z)}$$

$$H_z^0 = [C^0 I_0(\gamma r) + D^0 K_0(\gamma r)] e^{j(\omega t - \beta z)}$$

where A^0, B^0, C^0, D^0 = constants to be determined, superscript denotes "outside". Expressing the other components in terms E_z^0 and H_z^0, we obtain

$$E_r^0 = \frac{j\beta}{\gamma} [A^0 I_1(\gamma r) - B^0 K_1(\gamma r)] e^{j(\omega t - \beta z)}$$

$$E_\theta^0 = -\frac{j\omega\mu}{\gamma}[C^0 I_1(\gamma r) - D^0 K_1(\gamma r)]\, e^{j(\omega t - \beta z)}$$

$$H_r^0 = \frac{j\beta}{\gamma}[C^0 I_1(\gamma r) - D^0 K_1(\gamma r)]\, e^{j(\omega t - \beta z)}$$

$$H_\theta^0 = \frac{j\omega\epsilon}{\gamma}[A^0 I_1(\gamma r) - B^0 K_1(\gamma r)]\, e^{j(\omega t - \beta z)}$$

II.2 BOUNDARY CONDITIONS

1. Helix represents a surface that conducts only along the direction specified by pitch angle ψ; tangential electric field is perpendicular to helix at $r = a$:

$$E_z^i \sin \psi + E_\theta^i \cos \psi = 0$$
$$E_z^0 \sin \psi + E_\theta^0 \cos \psi = 0$$

2. Component of tangential electric field normal to the direction of ψ is continuous across cylinder at $r = a$:

$$E_z^i \cos \psi - E_\theta^i \sin \psi = E_z^0 \cos \psi - E_\theta^0 \sin \psi$$

3. Component of tangential magnetic field along ψ must be continuous at $r = a$ (no current flow normal to direction of ψ):

$$H_z^i \sin \psi + H_\theta^i \cos \psi = H_z^0 \sin \psi + H_\theta^0 \cos \psi$$

4. At the shield $r = b$, tangential electric field and normal magnetic field must be zero:

$$E_z^0 = 0$$
$$E_\theta^0 = 0$$
$$H_r^0 = 0$$

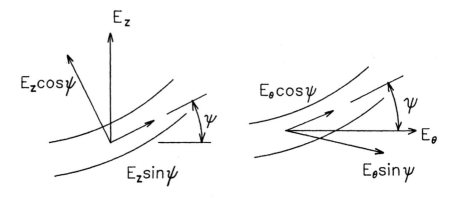

Fig. 45 Pitch Angle ψ and Tangential Electric Field of Helix

Evaluating all boundary conditions in the same sequence, we obtain seven equations in six unknown constants plus γ:

$$A^i I_0(\gamma a) \sin \psi - \frac{j\omega\mu}{\gamma} C^i I_1(\gamma a) \cos \psi = 0 \tag{II.1a}$$

$$[A^0 I_0(\gamma a) + B^0 K_0(\gamma a)] \sin \psi$$
$$- \frac{j\omega\mu}{\gamma} \cos \psi \, [C^0 I_1(\gamma a) - D^0 K_1(\gamma a)] = 0 \tag{II.1b}$$

$$A^i I_0(\gamma a) \cos \psi + \frac{j\omega\mu}{\gamma} C^i I_1(\gamma a) \sin \psi$$
$$= [A^0 I_0(\gamma a) + B^0 K_0(\gamma a)] \cos \psi \tag{II.2}$$
$$+ \frac{j\omega\mu}{\gamma} [C^0 I_1(\gamma a) - D^0 K_1(\gamma a)] \sin \psi$$

$$C^i I_0(\gamma a) \sin \psi + \frac{j\omega\epsilon}{\gamma} A^i I_1(\gamma a) \cos \psi$$
$$= [C^0 I_0(\gamma a) + D^0 K_0(\gamma a)] \sin \psi \tag{II.3}$$
$$+ \frac{j\omega\epsilon}{\gamma} [A^0 I_1(\gamma a) - B^0 K_1(\gamma a)] \cos \psi$$

$$A^0 I_0(\gamma b) + B^0 K_0(\gamma b) = 0 \tag{II.4a}$$

$$C^0 I_1(\gamma b) - D^0 K_1(\gamma b) = 0 \tag{II.4b}$$

$$C^0 I_1(\gamma b) - D^0 K_1(\gamma b) = 0 \tag{II.4c}$$

Starting from (II.4a)–(II.4c) and then proceeding to (II.1a)–(II.1b) and (II.2), evaluate all the unknown constants in terms of A^i. Then use (II.3) to evaluate γ. Introduce two shorthand notations to simplify the mathematics:

$$\Delta_0 = \frac{I_0(\gamma a) I_0(\gamma b)}{I_0(\gamma b) K_0(\gamma a) - I_0(\gamma a) K_0(\gamma b)}$$

$$\Delta_1 = \frac{I_0(\gamma a) I_1(\gamma b)}{I_1(\gamma b) K_1(\gamma a) - I_1(\gamma a) K_1(\gamma b)}$$

and

$$A^0 = \frac{A^i}{1 - \dfrac{I_0(\gamma b) K_0(\gamma a)}{I_0(\gamma a) K_0(\gamma b)}} = - \frac{K_0(\gamma b)}{I_0(\gamma b)} \Delta_0 \, A^i$$

$$B^0 = -A^0 \frac{I_0(\gamma b)}{K_0(\gamma b)} = + \Delta_0 A^i$$

$$C^0 = \frac{I_0(\gamma a)\, \gamma (\tan\psi) A^i}{[I_1(\gamma a) - I_1(\gamma b) K_1(\gamma a)/K_1(\gamma b)] j\omega\mu}$$

$$= \frac{j(\tan\psi)\,\gamma}{\omega\mu} \frac{K_1(\gamma b)}{I_1(\gamma b)} \Delta_1 A^i$$

$$D^0 = \frac{j\gamma\tan\psi}{\omega\mu} \Delta_1 A^i$$

$$C^i = \frac{I_0(\gamma a)}{I_1(\gamma a)} \gamma \frac{\tan\psi}{j\omega\mu} A^i = - \frac{j\gamma\tan\psi}{\omega\mu} \frac{I_0(\gamma a)}{I_1(\gamma a)} A^i$$

$$\omega^2\mu\epsilon\cot^2\psi = \gamma^2 \frac{I_1(\gamma b) I_0(\gamma a)[I_0(\gamma a) K_0(\gamma b) - I_0(\gamma b) K_0(\gamma a)]}{I_0(\gamma b) I_1(\gamma a)[I_1(\gamma a) K_1(\gamma b) - I_1(\gamma b) K_1(\gamma a)]}$$

$$= \gamma^2 \frac{I_0(\gamma a)}{I_1(\gamma a)} \frac{\Delta_1}{\Delta_0}$$

Substituting the above constants into the appropriate equations, we obtain the following summary. (Superscript on A^i dropped, everything referenced to amplitude of E_z at $r = 0$.)

II.2.1 Inside Helix

$$E_z = A I_0(\gamma r) e^{j(\omega t - \beta z)}$$

$$E_r = jA \frac{\beta}{\gamma} I_1(\gamma r) e^{j(\omega t - \beta z)}$$

$$E_\theta = -A \frac{I_0(\gamma a)}{I_1(\gamma a)} (\tan \psi) I_1(\gamma r) e^{j(\omega t - \beta z)}$$

$$H_z = -jA \frac{\gamma}{\omega \mu} \frac{I_0(\gamma a)}{I_1(\gamma a)} (\tan \psi) I_0(\gamma r) e^{j(\omega t - \beta z)}$$

$$H_r = A \frac{\beta}{\omega \mu} \frac{I_0(\gamma a)}{I_1(\gamma a)} (\tan \psi) I_1(\gamma r) e^{j(\omega t - \beta z)}$$

$$H_\theta = jA \frac{\omega \epsilon}{\gamma} I_1(\gamma r) e^{j(\omega t - \beta z)}$$

II.2.2 Outside Helix

$$E_z = A \Delta_0 \left[K_0(\gamma r) - \frac{K_0(\gamma b)}{I_0(\gamma b)} I_0(\gamma r) \right] e^{j(\omega t - \beta z)}$$

$$E_r = -jA \frac{\beta}{\gamma} \Delta_0 \left[K_1(\gamma r) + \frac{K_0(\gamma b)}{I_0(\gamma b)} I_1(\gamma r) \right] e^{j(\omega t - \beta z)}$$

$$E_\theta = -A (\tan \psi) \Delta_1 \left[K_1(\gamma r) - \frac{K_1(\gamma b)}{I_1(\gamma b)} I_1(\gamma r) \right] e^{j(\omega t - \beta z)}$$

$$H_z = jA \frac{\gamma}{\omega \mu} (\tan \psi) \Delta_1 \left[K_0(\gamma r) + \frac{K_1(\gamma b)}{I_1(\gamma b)} I_0(\gamma r) \right] e^{j(\omega t - \beta z)}$$

$$H_r = A \frac{\beta}{\omega \mu} (\tan \psi) \Delta_1 \left[K_1(\gamma r) - \frac{K_1(\gamma b)}{I_1(\gamma b)} I_1(\gamma r) \right] e^{j(\omega t - \beta z)}$$

$$H_\theta = -jA \frac{\omega\epsilon}{\gamma} \Delta_0 \left[K_1(\gamma r) + \frac{K_0(\gamma b)}{I_0(\gamma b)} I_1(\gamma r) \right] e^{j(\omega t - \beta z)}$$

$$\beta_0^2 \cot^2 \psi = \gamma^2 \frac{I_0(\gamma a)}{I_1(\gamma a)} \frac{\Delta_1}{\Delta_0}$$

Appendix III
Computer Programs

This section contains program listings (in HP BASIC written for the HP Series 200 computers) and sample outputs for three computer programs. The first one allows the designer to examine Butterworth filter characteristics and interactively change any of the filter parameters such as center frequency, number of sections, unloaded Q *et cetera*, and immediately judge their effects on insertion loss and out-of-band attenuation. The next two programs design optimum conventional helical resonators for shields of circular or square cross section, as outlined in APPENDIX I and [3]. In addition, the dielectric constant and loss tangent can be specified for the resonator medium, to evaluate changes in unloaded Q and resonant frequency for a resonator filled with dielectric.

A typical design sequence would involve running the Butterworth program to determine the number of sections and required unloaded Q to meet the given filter specifications. The next step would be to run one of the HELICAL programs (depending on what shield cross section was desired) to obtain the resonator dimensions for the required unloaded Q. Several iterations of running the two programs might be required to examine different trade-offs, such as using more sections of lower Q *versus* fewer sections of high Q resonators.

No claim is made to the originality of these programs. They are based on published, publicly available formulas and many similar programs probably exist throughout the industry. I include them in this book because I wrote and verified them and find them useful and accurate in my work as a filter designer. My hope is that they will perform the same function for others.

III.1   BUTTERWORTH PROGRAM

This program requires five inputs and generates three outputs. The inputs are: filter center frequency, bandwidth, number of sections, unloaded Q of each section, and the frequency at which it is desired to know filter attenuation. Since many of these inputs are unknown design parameters, an initial intelligent guess is required to start the design process. The three outputs are insertion loss at the filter center frequency, attenuation at the desired frequency relative to the loss at the center frequency, and the total insertion loss at the desired frequency. After all the filter parameters are displayed on the screen, the designer can change any or all of the input parameters to obtain a new insertion loss and skirt attenuation. The procedure can be repeated as many times as necessary to fine-tune the filter parameters. The latest calculation can be printed out at any time to an HPIB (IEEE-488) printer at address 701. All the frequency inputs are in MHz, maximum number of sections is 8 and insertion loss is calculated by the group delay approximation.

In addition to the previous calculations, the program performs some error checking on the input data to determine if the filter is realizable. The three error conditions flagged are: unloaded Q less than loaded Q, bandwidth wider than twice the center frequency and more than eight resonant sections. Sample calculation: Suppose we want to characterize a filter of 520 MHz center frequency, 7 MHz 3 dB bandwidth, constructed of four resonators, each with an unloaded Q of 600. We would like to know the midband insertion loss and attenuation at 512.8 MHz. After entering the five input parameters, the results are as follows:

CENTER FREQ, BANDWIDTH, N, UNLOADED Q
520.000   7.000 4   600.00
FREQUENCY FOR WHICH ATTENUATION DESIRED
512.800
MIDBAND INSERTION LOSS   = 2.725 dB
ATTENUATION   = 25.32 dB
ATTENUATION (INCL. INS LOSS) = 28.04 dB
_ _

Changing the Q to 700 would decrease insertion loss to 2.32 dB.

Program Listing

```
10    ! ***** BUTTERWORTH ***** APR 11/1985
20    !CHARACTERIZATION OF BUTTERWORTH FILTERS UP TO 8th ORDER"
30    !RESTRICTIONS:Q<9999.99,N<9,CF<9999.99,BW<9999.99
40    PRINT CHR$(12)
50    DISP CHR$(128)
60    PRINT CHR$(128)
70    ALLOCATE Qmin(9)
80    PRINT "BUTTERWORTH BANDPASS FILTER ANALYSIS"
90    PRINT "********************************* "
100   PRINT
110   PRINT "DO YOU WANT INSTRUCTIONS (Y/N)?"
120   INPUT A$
130   IF A$<>"Y" THEN GOTO 310
140   PRINT "_ _ _ _ _ _ _ _ _ _ _ _ _ _ _ _ _ _ _ _ _ _ _ _"
150   PRINT "THIS PROGRAM WILL CALCULATE THE MIDBAND"
160   PRINT "INSERTION LOSS AND ATTENUATION AT SOME"
170   PRINT "DESIRED FREQUENCY. THE INPUTS THAT THE PROGRAM"
180   PRINT "NEEDS ARE:"
190   PRINT "      1)CENTER FREQUENCY IN MHz"
200   PRINT "      2)3 dB BANDWIDTH IN MHz"
210   PRINT "      3)NUMBER OF RESONANT SECTIONS (UP TO 8)"
220   PRINT "      4)UNLOADED QUALITY FACTOR OF EACH SECTION"
```

```
230    PRINT "(ENTER THESE FOUR PARAMETERS ON ONE LINE"
240    PRINT " SEPARATED BY COMMAS)"
250    PRINT "       5)FREQUENCY AT WHICH ATTENUATION"
260    PRINT "       IS TO BE CALCULATED"
270    PRINT "(ENTER THIS NUMBER IN MHz ON SEPARATE LINE"
280    PRINT " AS PROMPTED BY COMPUTER)"
290    PRINT "- - - - - - - - - - - - - - - - - - - - - - - - -"
300    PRINT
310    PRINT "ENTER CENTER FREQ, BANDWIDTH, N, UNLOADED
       Q"
320    DISP CHR$(133)
330    INPUT Cf,Bw,N,Qu
340    IF Bw>2*Cf OR N>8 OR Qu<0. OR Bw<0 OR N<0 THEN
350         BEEP 100,.5
360         PRINT "INVALID DATA, TRY AGAIN"
370         GOTO 840
380         END IF
390    PRINT USING
       "5X,DDDDD.DDD,4X,DDDD.DDD,3X,D,3X,DDDD.DD";
       Cf,Bw,N,Qu
400    PRINT "ENTER FREQUENCY FOR WHICH ATTENUATION
       DESIRED"
410    INPUT W
420    DISP CHR$(128)
430    PRINT USING "5X,DDDDD.DDD";W
440    Q_loaded = Cf/Bw
450    !
460    ! MINIMUM Q'S FOR BUTTERWORTH DESIGN
470    !
480    Qmin(1) = 1
490    Qmin(2) = 1.4
500    Qmin(3) = 2.0
510    Qmin(4) = 2.6
520    Qmin(5) = 3.24
530    Qmin(6) = 3.86
540    Qmin(7) = 4.6
550    Qmin(8) = 5.1
560    If Qu<Q_loaded*Qmin(N) THEN
570         BEEP 2000,.2
580         BEEP 200,.2
590         PRINT "FILTER NONREALIZABLE, Q TOO LOW"
600         Il = 999.999
610         At = 999.99
```

```
620         Att = 999.99
630         GOTO 840
640         END IF
650     !
660     !CALCULATE INSERTION LOSS USING GROUP DELAY
        APPROXIMATION
670     !
680     Group_delay = 0.
690     For K = 1 TO N
700         Group_delay = Group_delay + ABS(COS(((2*K + N − 10)/
            N)*PI/2))
710         NEXT K
720     Il = 8.686*((Q_loaded/Qu) + .4*(Q_loaded/Qu)^2)*Group_delay
730     !
740     !CALCULATE ATTENUATION BY USING LOW-PASS TO BAND-
        PASS TRANSFORMATION"
750     !
760     At = 10*LGT(1.0 + ((W*W − Cf*Cf)/(Bw*W))^(2.0*N))
770     If At>999 THEN At = 999.99
780     Att = At + Il
790     IF Att>999 THEN Att = 999.99
800     PRINT "− − − − − − − − − − − − − − − − − − − − − − − − −"
810     PRINT USING "33A,DDD.DD";"MIDBAND INSERTION LOSS
        = ",Il;" dB"
820     PRINT USING "33A,DDD.DD";"ATTENUATION    = ",At;" dB"
830     PRINT USING "33A,DDD.DD";"ATTENUATION
        (INCL.INS.LOSS) = ",Att;" dB"
840     PRINT " = = = = = = = = = = = = = = = = = = = = = = = = ="
850     ON KEY 5 LABEL "CONTINUE" GOTO 310
860     ON KEY 6 LABEL "TO PRINTER" GOTO 940
870     ON KEY 9 LABEL "STOP" GOTO 1210
880     ON KEY 4 LABEL "CHANGE ATT FREQ" GOTO 1060
890     ON KEY 1 LABEL "CHANGE BW" GOTO 1080
900     ON KEY 2 LABEL "CHANGE N" GOTO 1100
910     ON KEY 0 LABEL "CHANGE FREQ" GOTO 1130
920     ON KEY 3 LABEL "CHANGE Q" GOTO 1150
930     GOTO 850
940     PRINTER IS 701
950     PRINT "     CENTER FREQ, BANDWIDTH, N, UNLOADED Q"
960     PRINT USING
        "5X,DDDDD.DDD,4X,DDDD.DDD,4X,D,3X,DDDD.DD";
        Cf,Bw,N,Qu
```

92

```
970     PRINT "      FREQUENCY FOR WHICH ATTENUATION
        DESIRED"
980     PRINT USING "5X,DDDDD.DDD";W
990     PRINT USING "33A,DDD.DDD";"MIDBAND INSERTION LOSS
        = ",Il;" dB"
1000    PRINT USING "33A,DDD.DD";"ATTENUATION   = ",At;" dB"
1010    PRINT USING "33A,DDD.DD";"ATTENUATION (INCL.INS
        LOSS) = ",Att;" dB"
1020    PRINT "- - - - - - - - - - - - - - - - - - - - - - - -"
1030    PRINT " "
1040    PRINTER IS 1
1050    GOTO 850
1060    INPUT "NEW ATTENUATION FREQUENCY?",W
1070    GOTO 1160
1080    INPUT "NEW 3 dB BANDWIDTH",Bw
1090    GOTO 1160
1100    INPUT "NEW NUMBER OF RESONATORS?",N
1110    IF N>8 THEN GOTO 340
1120    GOTO 1160
1130    INPUT "NEW CENTER FREQUENCY?",Cf
1140    GOTO 1160
1150    INPUT "NEW UNLOADED Q?",Qu
1160    PRINT "ENTER CENTER FREQ,BANDWIDTH, N ,UNLOADED
        Q"
1170    PRINT USING
        "5X,DDDDD.DDD,4X,DDDD.DDD,3X,D,3X,DDDD.DD";
        Cf,Bw,N,Qu
1180    PRINT "ENTER FREQUENCY FOR WHICH ATTENUATION
        DESIRED"
1190    PRINT USING "5X,DDDDD.DDD";W
1200    GOTO 440
1210    END
```

III.2 HELICAL-C PROGRAM

This program calculates all the relevant mechanical dimensions of a conventional optimal helical resonator enclosed in a shield of circular cross section. Both shield and helix are assumed to be made of copper. All dimensions are in metric units (cm). The two required inputs are: inside diameter of the shield and the resonant frequency in MHz. The program then comes up with eight calculated output parameters: unloaded Q, total resonator (not helix) height, mean helix diameter, pitch, number of turns, line characteristic impedance, wire diameter, and the closest wire gauge if between 1 and 40. [Knowledge of line characteristic impedance is useful in estimating the tuning capacitance required to lower the resonant frequency by a given amount because the resonator can be modeled as a section of transmission line of length (number of turns divided by pitch) terminated in the tuning capacitance. The frequency at which the input impedance of this combination is zero is the resonant frequency.] Next, the designer has a choice of filling the resonator with dielectric. If he chooses to do so, the dielectric constant and dissipation factor have to be supplied as inputs. The program then calculates the new resonant frequency, unloaded Q, and characteristic impedance. Again, the results can be printed out to a printer at HPIB address 701 or an RS232 printer by including lines 570 to 590 and 800, and deleting lines 600 and 810.

In contrast to the BUTTERWORTH program, there is no checking of input data for resonator realizability; the designer must exercise engineering judgment to determine if the output data is valid. For example, total number of turns less than two, or mean helix diameter less than twice the wire diameter should signal the designer that a helical resonator based on his input data may not be realizable.

Let us design a resonator for operation at 250 MHz, enclosed in a circular shield of inner diameter of 3.2 cm:

SHLD INNER DIA D	= 3.200cm	INPUT SUPPLIED BY
FREQUENCY	= 250.000MHz	DESIGNER

```
************************************
```

UNLOADED Q	= 995.1	
RESONATOR HEIGHT H	= 4.25cm	COMPUTER-
MEAN HELIX DIA. d	= 1.76cm	GENERATED OUTPUT
PITCH	= 2.29turns/cm	SEE APPENDIX I FOR
NUMBER OF TURNS	= 6.1	DEFINITIONS OF
CHAR. IMPEDANCE	= 310.51ohms	SYMBOLS
WIRE DIAMETER g	= .219cm	
(CLOSEST WIRE GAGE IS 11 AWG)		

Filled with polypropylene (dielectric constant = 2.6, dissipation factor = 0.0005), the new resonant frequency would be 155.04 MHz, unloaded Q would degrade to 664.5, and characteristic impedance would be lowered to 192.6 ohms.

Program Listing

```
10     ! *** HELICAL_C *** May 8/1985
20     PRINT CHR$(12)
30     Flag = 0
40     OFF KEY
50     DEG
60     DISP CHR$(129)
70     PRINT TABXY(3,5),"PROGRAM CALCULATES DIMENSIONS"
80     PRINT TABXY(3,6),"OF OPTIMAL HELICAL RESONATOR"
90     PRINT TABXY(3,7),"(CIRCULAR SHIELD CROSS SECTION)"
100    PRINT TABXY(3,9),"ENTER INNER DIAMETER OF"
110    PRINT TABXY(3,10),"SHIELD 'D' [cm]"
120    INPUT " 'D' DIMENSION = ?[cm] ",D
130    PRINT TABXY(3,11),"ENTER FREQUENCY IN MHz"
140    INPUT " FREQUENCY = ?[MHz] ",F
150    PRINT TABXY(3,9),"                        "
160    PRINT TABXY(3,11),"                        "
170    PRINT TABXY(3,8)
180    PRINT "SHLD INNER DIA 'D' = ";D;"cm           "
190    PRINT USING "11A,DDDD.DDD";"FREQUENCY =
          ";F;"MHz           "
200    IF Flag = 1 THEN
210      PRINT "DIELECTRIC Er = ";Er;"LOSS FACT = ";Df
220    END IF
230    PRINT "*********************************"
240    PRINT "RESULTING PARAMETERS ARE:        "
250    IF Flag = 1 THEN GOTO 350
260    S = D/1.2
270    Q = 23.6*S*SQR(F)
280    Turns = 4064/(F*S)
290    Pitch = 4064/(S*S*F)
300    Zed = 207010/(F*S)
310    D_ = .66*S
320    H = 1.592*S
```

```
330    G = 1./(2*Pitch)
340    CALL Gage_(G,Gage)
350    PRINT USING "19A,DDDDD.D";"UNLOADED
       Q          = ";Q;"     "
360    PRINT USING "19A,DD.DD";"RESONATOR HEIGHT H
       = ";H;"cm      "
370    PRINT USING "19A,DD.DD";"MEAN HELIX DIA. d
       = ";D_;"cm        "
380    PRINT USING
       "19A,DDD.DD";"PITCH          = ";Pitch;"turns/cm    "
390    PRINT USING "19A,DDD.D";"NUMBER OF
       TURNS   = ";Turns;"     "
400    IF Flag = 1 THEN Zed = Zed/SQR(Er)
410    PRINT USING "19A,DDDDD.DD";"CHAR.
       IMPEDANCE   = ";Zed;"ohms      "
420    PRINT USING "19A,DD.DDD";"WIRE DIAMETER g
       = ";G;"cm"
430    IF Gage = 0 THEN GOTO 460
440    PRINT USING "22A,DDD";"(CLOSEST WIRE GAGE IS";Gage;"
       AWG)"
450    IF Flag = 1 THEN GOTO 470
460    WAIT 1.5
470    ON KEY 0 LABEL "PRINT" GOTO 570
480    ON KEY 5 LABEL "REPEAT" GOTO 20
490    ON KEY 1 LABEL "STOP" GOTO 920
500    IF Flag = 1 THEN
510      OFF KEY 7
520      GOTO 470
530      END IF
540    ON KEY 7 LABEL "DIELECTRIC" GOTO 840
550    GOTO 470
560    GOTO 470
570    ! PRINTER IS 9          !RS-232
580    ! CONTROL 9,4;7         !RS-232
590    ! OUTPUT 9;CHR$(15)     !RS-232
600    PRINTER IS 701          !IEEE-488
610    PRINT USING 630;"SHLD INNER DIA D  = ";D;"cm"
620    PRINT USING 630;"FREQUENCY        = ";F;"MHz"
630    IMAGE 18A,DDDD.DDD,3A
640    IF Flag = 1 THEN
650      PRINT "DIELECTRIC Er = ";Er;"LOSS FACT = ";Df
```

```
660     END IF
670     PRINT "*******************************"
680     PRINT USING "19A,DDDDD.D";"UNLOADED
        Q       =";Q;"          "
690     PRINT USING "19A,DD.DD";"RESONATOR HEIGHT H
        =";H;"cm          "
700     PRINT USING "19A,DD.DD";"MEAN HELIX DIA. d
        =";D_;"cm          "
710     PRINT USING
        "19A,DDD.DD";"PITCH           =";Pitch;"turns/cm          "
720     PRINT USING "19A,DDD.D";"NUMBER OF
        TURNS       =";Turns;"          "
730     PRINT USING "19A,DDDDD.DD";"CHAR.
        IMPEDANCE       =";Zed;"ohms"
740     PRINT USING "19A,DD.DDD";"WIRE DIAMETER       g
        =";G;"cm"
750     IF Gage=0 THEN GOTO 800
760     PRINT USING "22A,DDD";"(CLOSEST WIRE GAGE IS";Gage;"
        AWG)"
770     PRINT
780     PRINT
790     PRINT
800     ! OUTPUT 9;CHR$(18)          !RS-232
810     PRINTER IS 1
820     GOTO 470
830     DISP CHR$(128)
840     !DIELECTRIC CALCULATION
850     INPUT "ENTER DIELECTRIC CONSTANT",Er
860     INPUT "ENTER DISSIPATION FACTOR",Df
870     F=F/SQR(Er)
880     Q=1/(1/Q+Df)
890     Flag=1
900     PRINT TABXY(1,6)
910     GOTO 180
920     END
930     !
940     !
950     SUB Gage_(G,Gage)
960     G=10*G
970     IF G<8.252 THEN Gage=1
980     IF G<6.95 THEN Gage=2
```

```
990    IF G<6.185 THEN Gage = 3
1000   IF G<5.508 THEN Gage = 4
1010   IF G<4.905 THEN Gage = 5
1020   IF G<4.358 THEN Gage = 6
1030   IF G<3.890 THEN Gage = 7
1040   IF G<3.465 THEN Gage = 8
1050   IF G<3.085 THEN Gage = 9
1060   IF G<2.747 THEN Gage = 10
1070   IF G<2.446 THEN Gage = 11
1080   IF G<2.177 THEN Gage = 12
1090   IF G<1.940 THEN Gage = 13
1100   IF G<1.730 THEN Gage = 14
1110   IF G<1.540 THEN Gage = 15
1120   IF G<1.370 THEN Gage = 16
1130   IF G<1.220 THEN Gage = 17
1140   IF G<1.085 THEN Gage = 18
1150   IF G<.9660 THEN Gage = 19
1160   IF G<.8625 THEN Gage = 20
1170   IF G<.7685 THEN Gage = 21
1180   IF G<.6835 THEN Gage = 22
1190   IF G<.6085 THEN Gage = 23
1200   IF G<.5425 THEN Gage = 24
1210   IF G<.4830 THEN Gage = 25
1220   IF G<.4295 THEN Gage = 26
1230   IF G<.3825 THEN Gage = 27
1240   IF G<.3405 THEN Gage = 28
1250   IF G<.3035 THEN Gage = 29
1260   IF G<.2705 THEN Gage = 30
1270   IF G<.2400 THEN Gage = 31
1280   IF G<.2145 THEN Gage = 32
1290   IF G<.1915 THEN Gage = 33
1300   IF G<.1700 THEN Gage = 34
1310   IF G<.1510 THEN Gage = 35
1320   IF G<.1345 THEN Gage = 36
1330   IF G<.1205 THEN Gage = 37
1340   IF G<.1080 THEN Gage = 38
1350   IF G<.09545 THEN Gage = 39
1360   IF G<.08380 THEN Gage = 40
1370   G = G/10
1380   SUBEND
```

III.3 HELICAL-S PROGRAM

This program is identical to HELICAL-C, except that the resonator is enclosed in a shield of square cross section. (Program lines which are different from HELICAL-C are lines 90–180, 260 and 610.) Sample output for a 450 MHz resonator in a shield of 1.5 cm width is as follows:

```
LENGTH OF SIDE S          =    1.500cm
FREQUENCY                 = 450.000MHz
**********************************************
UNLOADED Q                = 750.9
RESONATOR HEIGHT H        = 2.39cm
MEAN HELIX DIA. d         = .99cm
PITCH                     = 4.01turns/cm
NUMBER OF TURNS           = 6.0
CHAR. IMPEDANCE           = 306.68ohms
WIRE DIAMETER g           = 0.125cm
(CLOSEST WIRE GAGE IS 16 AWG)
```

Filled with polypropylene (dielectric constant = 2.6, dissipation factor = 0.0005), new resonant frequency is 279.08 MHz, Q = 546.0, and characteristic impedance = 190.2 ohms.

Program Listing

```
10     ! *** HELICAL_S *** May 8/1985
20     PRINT CHR$(12)
30     Flag = 0
40     OFF KEY
50     DEG
60     DISP CHR$(129)
70     PRINT TABXY(3,5),"PROGRAM CALCULATES DIMENSIONS"
80     PRINT TABXY(3,6),"OF OPTIMAL HELICAL RESONATOR"
90     PRINT TABXY(3,7),"(SQUARE SHIELD CROSS SECTION)"
100    PRINT TABXY(3,9),"ENTER DIMENSION OF"
110    PRINT TABXY(3,10),"SIDE 'S' [cm]"
120    INPUT " 'S' DIMENSION = ?[cm] ",S
130    PRINT TABXY(3,11),"ENTER FREQUENCY IN MHz"
```

```
140    INPUT " FREQUENCY = ?[MHz] ",F
150    PRINT TABXY(3,9),"                           "
160    PRINT TABXY(3,11),"                           "
170    PRINT TABXY(3,8)
180    PRINT "LENGTH OF SIDE 'S' = ";S;"cm        "
190    PRINT USING "11A,DDDD.DDD";"FREQUENCY = ";F;"MHz "
200    IF Flag = 1 THEN
210    PRINT "DIELECTRIC Er = ";Er;"LOSS FACT = ";Df
220    END IF
230    PRINT "******************************"
240    PRINT "RESULTING PARAMETERS ARE:        "
250    IF Flag = 1 THEN GOTO 350
260    !
270    Q = 23.6*S*SQR(F)
280    Turns = 4064/(F*S)
290    Pitch = 4064/(S*S*F)
300    Zed = 207010/(F*S)
310    D = .66*S
320    H = 1.592*S
330    G = 1./(2*Pitch)
340    CALL Gage_(G,Gage)
350    PRINT USING "19A,DDDDD.D";"UNLOADED
       Q          = ";Q;"      "
360    PRINT USING "19A,DD.DD";"RESONATOR HEIGHT H
       = ";H;"cm       "
370    PRINT USING "19A,DD.DD";"MEAN HELIX DIA. d
       = ";D;"cm        "
380    PRINT USING
       "19A,DDD.D";"PITCH            = ";Pitch;"turns/cm"
390    PRINT USING "19A,DDD.D";"NUMBER OF TURNS   = ";Turns
400    IF Flag = 1 THEN Zed = Zed/SQR(Er)
410    PRINT USING "19A,DDDDD.DD";"CHAR.
       IMPEDANCE   = ";Zed;"ohms"
420    PRINT USING "19A,DD.DDD";"WIRE DIAMETER   g
       = ";G;"cm"
430    IF Gage = 0 THEN GOTO 460
440    PRINT USING "22A,DDD";"(CLOSEST WIRE GAGE IS";Gage;"
       AWG)"
450    IF Flag = 1 THEN GOTO 470
460    WAIT 1.5
470    ON KEY 0 LABEL "PRINT" GOTO 570
```

```
480    ON KEY 5 LABEL "REPEAT" GOTO 20
490    ON KEY 1 LABEL "STOP" GOTO 920
500    IF Flag = 1 THEN
510      OFF KEY 7
520      GOTO 470
530      END IF
540    ON KEY 7 LABEL "DIELECTRIC" GOTO 840
550    GOTO 470
560    GOTO 470
570      !PRINTER IS 9          !RS-232
580      !CONTROL 9,4;7         !RS-232
590      !OUTPUT 9;CHR$(15)     !RS-232
600    PRINTER IS 701           !IEEE-488
610    PRINT USING 630;"LENGTH OF SIDE S  = ";S;"cm"
620    PRINT USING 630;"FREQUENCY          = ";F;"MHz"
630    IMAGE 18A,DDDD.DDD,3A
640    IF Flag = 1 THEN
650      PRINT "DIELECTRIC Er = ";Er;"LOSS FACT = ";Df
660      END IF
670    PRINT "**********************************"
680    PRINT USING "19A,DDDDD.D";"UNLOADED Q       = ";Q
690    PRINT USING "19A,DD.DD";"RESONATOR HEIGHT H
       = ";H;"cm"
700    PRINT USING "19A,DD.DD";"MEAN HELIX DIA. d
       = ";D;"cm"
710    PRINT USING
       "19A,DDD.DD";"PITCH              = ";Pitch;"turns/cm"
720    PRINT USING "19A,DDD.D";"NUMBER OF
       TURNS     = ";Turns
730    PRINT USING "19A,DDDDD.DD";"CHAR.
       IMPEDANCE     = ";Zed;"ohms"
740    PRINT USING "19A,DD.DDD";"WIRE DIAMETER    g
       = ";G;"cm"
750    IF Gage = 0 THEN GOTO 770
760    PRINT USING "22A,DDD";"(CLOSEST WIRE GAGE IS";Gage;"
       AWG)"
770    PRINT
780    PRINT
790    PRINT
800      !OUTPUT 9;CHR$(18)      !RS-232
810    PRINTER IS 1
820    GOTO 470
```

```
830    DISP CHR$(128)
840    ! DIELECTRIC CALCULATION
850    INPUT "ENTER DIELECTRIC CONSTANT",Er
860    INPUT "ENTER DISSIPATION FACTOR",Df
870    F = F/SQR(Er)
880    Q = 1/(1/Q + Df)
890    Flag = 1
900    PRINT TABXY(1,6)
910    GOTO 180
920    END
930    !
940    !
950    SUB Gage_(G,Gage)
960    G = 10*G
970    IF G<8.252 THEN Gage = 1
980    IF G<6.95 THEN Gage = 2
990    IF G<6.185 THEN Gage = 3
1000   IF G<5.508 THEN Gage = 4
1010   IF G<4.905 THEN Gage = 5
1020   IF G<4.358 THEN Gage = 6
1030   IF G<3.890 THEN Gage = 7
1040   IF G<3.465 THEN Gage = 8
1050   IF G<3.085 THEN Gage = 9
1060   IF G<2.747 THEN Gage = 10
1070   IF G<2.446 THEN Gage = 11
1080   IF G<2.177 THEN Gage = 12
1090   IF G<1.940 THEN Gage = 13
1100   IF G<1.730 THEN Gage = 14
1110   IF G<1.540 THEN Gage = 15
1120   IF G<1.370 THEN Gage = 16
1130   IF G<1.220 THEN Gage = 17
1140   IF G<1.085 THEN Gage = 18
1150   IF G<.9660 THEN Gage = 19
1160   IF G<.8625 THEN Gage = 20
1170   IF G<.7685 THEN Gage = 21
1180   IF G<.6835 THEN Gage = 22
1190   IF G<.6085 THEN Gage = 23
1200   IF G<.5425 THEN Gage = 24
1210   IF G<.4830 THEN Gage = 25
1220   IF G<.4295 THEN Gage = 26
1230   IF G<.3825 THEN Gage = 27
1240   IF G<.3405 THEN Gage = 28
```

```
1250   IF G<.3035 THEN Gage = 29
1260   IF G<.2705 THEN Gage = 30
1270   IF G<.2400 THEN Gage = 31
1280   IF G<.2145 THEN Gage = 32
1290   IF G<.1915 THEN Gage = 33
1300   IF G<.1700 THEN Gage = 34
1310   IF G<.1510 THEN Gage = 35
1320   IF G<.1345 THEN Gage = 36
1330   IF G<.1205 THEN Gage = 37
1340   IF G<.1080 THEN Gage = 38
1350   IF G<.09545 THEN Gage = 39
1360   IF G<.08380 THEN Gage = 40
1370   G = G/10
1380   SUBEND
```

Bibliography

1. MacAlpine, W.W., and R.O Schildknecht, "Coaxial Resonators with Helical Inner Conductor," *Proc. IRE*, Vol. 47, pp. 2099–2105, Dec. 1959.
2. Zverev, A.I., and H.J. Blinchikoff, "Realization of a Filter with Helical Components," *IRE Trans. Comp. Parts*, Vol. CP-8, pp. 99–110, Sept. 1961.
3. Zverev, A.I., *Handbook of Filter Synthesis*, John Wiley and Sons, New York, 1967, Ch. 9, pp. 499–521.
4. Dishal, M., "Alignment and Adjustment of Synchronously Tuned Multiple-Resonant Circuit Filters," *Elect. Commun.*, pp. 154–164, June 1952.
5. Cohen, M., "Design Techniques Utilizing Helical Line Resonators," *Microwave J.*, Vol. 8, pp. 69–73, May 1965.
6. Banzhai, F.G., "Miniature Helical Filters," Motorola Internal Technical Report, March 1971.
7. Fisk, J.R., "Helical Resonator Design Techniques," *QST*, pp. 11–14, June 1976.
8. Pierce, J.R., *Traveling-Wave Tubes*, D. Van Nostrand, Princeton, NJ, 1950.
9. Cutler, C.C., "Experimental Determination of Helical-Wave Properties," *Proc. IRE*, Vol. 36, pp. 230–233, Feb. 1948.
10. Phillips, R.S., "The Electromagnetic Field Produced by a Helix," *Quart. Appl. Math.* Vol. 8, No. 3, pp. 229–246, 1950.

11. Sichak, W., "Coaxial Line with Helical Inner Conductor," *Proc. IRE*, Vol. 42, pp. 1315–1319, Aug. 1954.
12. Bryant, J.H., "Some Wave Properties of Helical Conductors," *Elect. Commun.* Vol. 31, No. 1, pp. 50–56, March 1954.
13. Miley, D.J., and J.B. Beyer, "Field Analysis of Helical Resonators with Constant-Bandwidth Filter Applications," *IEEE Trans. Parts, Materials and Packaging*, Vol. PMP-5, No. 3, pp. 127–132, Sept. 1969.
14. Sensiper, S., "Electromagnetic Wave Propagation on Helical Structures," *Proc. IRE*, Vol. 43, pp. 149–161, Feb. 1955.
15. Webber, S.E., "Calculations of Wave Propagation on a Helix in the Attenuation Region," *Trans. IRE*, Vol. ED-1, pp. 35–39, Aug. 1954.
16. Atia, A.E., and A.E. Williams, "Measurements of Intercavity Couplings," *IEEE Trans. Microwave Theory Tech.*, Vol. MTT-23, No. 6, pp. 519–521, June 1975.
17. Sollfrey, W., "Wave Propagation on Helical Wires," *J. Appl. Phys.*, Vol. 22, No. 7, pp. 905–910, July 1951.
18. Stark, L., "Lower Modes of a Concentric Line Having a Helical Inner Conductor," *J. Appl. Phys.*, Vol. 25, No. 9, pp. 1155–1162, Sept. 1954.
19. Vander Haagen, G.A., "The Electrical Tuning of Helical Resonators," *Microwave J.*, Vol. 10, pp. 84–90, Aug. 1967.
20. Lammers, U.H.W, *et al.*, "Varactor Tuned Helical Resonators at UHF," *RADC-TR-76-138*, U.S. Air Force, internal report, May 1976.
21. Fraser, R., Motorola Canada, private communication.
22. Lind, L.F., and R.E. Massara, "Generalised Interdigital Helical Resonator Filter," *Electron. Lett.*, Vol. 8, No. 21, Oct. 1972.
23. Wanat, R.J., "Wide Bandwidth Helical Resonator Filter," US Pat. No. 4,284,966, assigned to Motorola, Inc., Aug. 18, 1981.
24. Vizmuller, P., "Helical Resonator Filter with Dielectric Apertures," US Pat. No. 4,365,221, assigned to Motorola, Inc., Dec. 21, 1982.

25. Popovski, G.N., and P. Vizmuller, "Helical Resonator Filter," US Pat. No. 4,374,370, assigned to Motorola, Inc., Feb. 15, 1983.
26. Shult, D., "Helical Resonator Having Variable Capacitor which Includes Windings of Reduced Diameter, as One Plate Thereof," US Pat. No. 3,621,484, assigned to Motorola, Inc., Nov. 16, 1971.
27. Wanat, R.J., "Practical Design of Helical Resonator Filters," Motorola, Inc., internal publication, March 1982.
28. Sundquist, J.R., "Interspersed Double Winding Helical Resonator with Connections to Cavity," US Pat. No. 3,936,776, assigned to Bell Telephone Laboratories, Feb. 3, 1976.
29. Vizmuller, P., "Folded-over Helical Resonator," US Pat. No. 4,422,058, assigned to Motorola, Inc., Dec. 20, 1983.
30. DiPiazza, G.C., and P. Onno, "50W CW Diode-Tuned UHF Filter," *Microwave J.*, Vol. 29, No. 10, p. 133, Oct. 1986.

Index

The Artech House Communication and Electronic Defense Library

The Artech House Antenna Library

Antennas by L.V. Blake
Shipboard Antennas by Preston E. Law, Jr.
Shipboard Electromagnetics by Preston E. Law, Jr.
Antenna Design Using Personal Computers by David M. Pozar
Microstrip Antennas by I.J. Bahl and P. Bhartia
Interference Suppression Techniques for Microwave Antennas and Transmitters by Ernest R. Freeman
Principles of Electromagnetic Compatibility by Bernhard E. Keiser
Practical Simulation of Radar Antennas and Radomes by Herbert L. Hirsch and Douglas C. Grove